Alphabet

Print a small letter of the alphabet from <u>a</u> to <u>m</u> beside its p̶... the line in each box. Circle the same letters each time you se̶e̶ t̶h̶e̶m̶ i̶n̶ t̶h̶e̶ words within the box. Draw the dot-to-dot pictures.

1.	Aa	(a)pron / (A)d(a) / (a)l(a)rm / (A)d(a)m / g(a)me
2.	B	bib / baby / Bill / cab / Bob
3.	C	cup / Carol / comic / clown / clock
4.	D	duck / did / road / Dad / Dave
5.	E	eagle / eggs / Eve / need / see
6.	F	fan / fly / leaf / Fred / cuff
7.	G	goat / eggs / Gale / bag / gong
8.	H	hat / Harry / much / hand / John
9.	I	iron / did / bib / kite / comic
10.	J	jet / Jack / jeep / Jim / joke
11.	K	kite / duck / Kim / kick / keep
12.	L	lion / doll / mail / lily / Lucy
13.	(dot-to-dot: W, A • • G, D, B • C • E • F •)	
14.	M	money / jam / May / worm / Mom
15.	(dot-to-dot: B, C, E, A, D, F, K, L, H, I, G, J)	

Alphabet

Print a small letter of the alphabet from <u>n</u> to <u>z</u> beside its partner letter on the line in each box. Circle the same letters each time you see them in the words within the box. Draw the dot-to-dot pictures.

1.	2.	3.
ⓝⓘⓝe suⓝ spooⓝ ⓝose Ⓝaⓝ **N**n	oak color off Opal sock **O**	pipe Peter pop jeep tape **P**
4.	5.	6.
queen quart quit goat quilt **Q**	rock tear ruler rose Roy **R**	seven dress socks Sue mouse **S**
7.	8.	9.
top goat Tom tent belt **T**	uniform plum duck unit upset **U**	vest Vera vase five stove **V**
10.	11.	12.
web Will row weave woman **W**	six fox ax box tax **X**	yawn yo-yo funny yacht sky **Y**
13.	14.	15.
	zoo buzz zebra zero jazz **Z**	

Consonant Sound: S

The word <u>sun</u> begins with the sound of <u>s</u>. Say the name of the picture in each box. If the name begins with the sound of <u>s</u>, print S on the line in the box.

1. S	2.	3.
4.	5.	6.
7.	8.	9.
10.	11.	12.
13.	14.	15.

The word <u>bus</u> ends with the sound of <u>s</u>. Say the name of the picture in each box. If the name ends with the sound of <u>s</u>, print s on the line in the box.

1. S	2.	3.
4.	5.	6.
7.	8.	9.
10.	11.	12.
13.	14.	15.

Consonant Sound: T

The word <u>top</u> begins with the sound of t. Say the name of the picture in each box. If the name begins with the sound of <u>t</u>, print T on the line in the box.

1.	2.	3.
4.	5.	6.
7.	8.	9.
10.	11.	12.
13.	14.	15.

The word <u>bat</u> ends with the sound of t. Say the name of the picture in each box. If the name ends with the sound of <u>t</u>, print t on the line in the box.

1.	2.	3.
4.	5.	6.
7.	8.	9.
10.	11.	12.
13.	14.	15.

Consonant Sound: B

The word <u>bag</u> begins with the sound of <u>b</u>. Say the name of the picture in each box. If the name begins with the sound of <u>b</u>, print B on the line in the box.

The word <u>web</u> ends with the sound of <u>b</u>. Say the name of the picture in each box. If the name ends with the sound of <u>b</u>, print <u>b</u> on the line in the box.

Consonant Sounds: B, S, T

Play Tic-Tac-Toe. Draw a line through the three pictures in a row that begin with the same sound. You may find more than one row in a game.

1.

2.

3.

4.

5.

6.

Consonant Sounds: H, J

The word <u>hat</u> begins with the sound of <u>h</u>. Say the name of the picture in each box. If the name begins with the sound of <u>h</u>, print H on the line in the box.

1.	2.	3.
4.	5.	6.
7.	8.	9.
10.	11.	12.
13.	14.	15.

The word <u>jeep</u> begins with the sound of <u>j</u>. Say the name of the picture in each box. If the name begins with the sound of <u>j</u>, print J on the line in the box.

1.	2.	3.
4.	5.	6.
7.	8.	9.
10.	11.	12.
13.	14.	15.

Consonant Sound: M

The word <u>mail</u> begins with the sound of <u>m</u>. Say the name of the picture in each box. If the name begins with the sound of <u>m</u>, print **M** on the line in the box.

1. $\mathbb{M}$	2. _____	3. _____
4. _____	5. _____	6. _____
7. _____	8. _____	9. _____
10. _____	11. _____	12. _____
13. _____	14. _____	15. _____

The word <u>gem</u> ends with the sound of <u>m</u>. Say the name of the picture in each box. If the name ends with the sound of <u>m</u>, print <u>m</u> on the line in the box.

1. m	2. _____	3. _____
4. _____	5. _____	6. _____
7. _____	8. _____	9. _____
10. _____	11. _____	12. _____
13. _____	14. _____	15. _____

Consonant Sound: K

The word <u>k</u>ite begins with the sound of k. Say the name of the picture in each box. If the name begins with the sound of <u>k</u>, print K on the line in the box.

1. K	2. ___	3. ___
4. ___	5. ___	6. ___
7. ___	8. ___	9. ___
10. ___	11. ___	12. ___
13. ___	14. ___	15. ___

The word blo<u>ck</u> ends with the sound of k. Say the name of the picture in each box. If the name ends with the sound of <u>k</u>, print k on the line in the box.

1. k	2. ___	3. ___
4. ___	5. ___	6. ___
7. ___	8. ___	9. ___
10. ___	11. ___	12. ___
13. ___	14. ___	15. ___

Consonant Sounds: H, J, K, M

Play Tic-Tac-Toe. Draw a line through the three pictures in a row that begin with the same sound. You may find more than one row in a game.

Consonant Sound: F

The word fish begins with the sound of f. Say the name of the picture in each box. If the name begins with the sound of f, print F on the line in the box.

The word leaf ends with the sound of f. Say the name of the picture in each box. If the name ends with the sound of f, print f on the line in the box.

Consonant Sound: G

The word <u>goat</u> begins with the sound of <u>g</u>. Say the name of the picture in each box. If the name begins with the sound of <u>g</u>, print <u>G</u> on the line in the box.

1. G	2.	3.
4.	5.	6.
7.	8.	9.
10.	11.	12.
13.	14.	15.

The word <u>pig</u> ends with the sound of <u>g</u>. Say the name of the picture in each box. If the name ends with the sound of <u>g</u>, print <u>g</u> on the line in the box.

1. g	2.	3.
4.	5.	6.
7.	8.	9.
10.	11.	12.
13.	14.	15.

Consonant Sound: D

The word <u>dog</u> begins with the sound of <u>d</u>. Say the name of the picture in each box. If the name begins with the sound of <u>d</u>, print <u>D</u> on the line in the box.

1.	D	2.		3.	
4.		5.		6.	
7.		8.		9.	
10.		11.		12.	
13.		14.		15.	

The word <u>bud</u> ends with the sound of <u>d</u>. Say the name of the picture in each box. If the name ends with the sound of <u>d</u>, print <u>d</u> on the line in the box.

1.	d	2.		3.	
4.		5.		6.	
7.		8.		9.	
10.		11.		12.	
13.		14.		15.	

Consonant Sound: L

The word <u>lamp</u> begins with the sound of l. Say the name of the picture in each box. If the name begins with the sound of l, print L on the line in the box.

1. L	2.	3.
4.	5.	6.
7.	8.	9.
10.	11.	12.
13.	14.	15.

The word <u>mail</u> ends with the sound of l. Say the name of the picture in each box. If the name ends with the sound of l, print l on the line in the box.

1. l	2.	3.
4.	5.	6.
7.	8.	9.
10.	11.	12.
13.	14.	15.

Consonant Sounds: D, F, G, L

Say the name of the picture in each box. Print the letters of the beginning and ending sounds on the lines under each picture.

1.	2.	3.
g m		

4.	5.	6.

7.	8.	9.

10.	11.	12.

Consonant Sound: N

The word <u>nest</u> begins with the sound of <u>n</u>. Say the name of the picture in each box. If the name begins with the sound of <u>n</u>, print <u>N</u> on the line in the box.

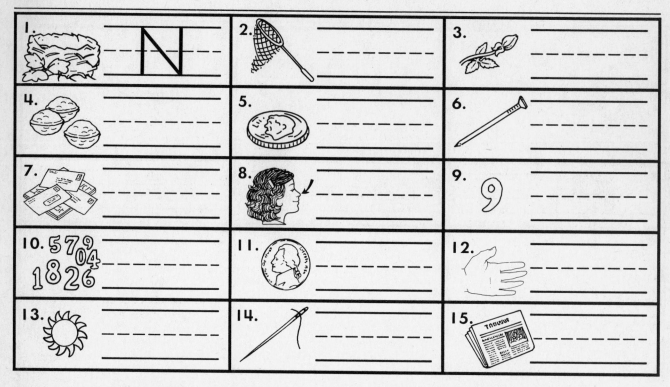

The word <u>fan</u> ends with the sound of <u>n</u>. Say the name of the picture in each box. If the name ends with the sound of <u>n</u>, print <u>n</u> on the line in the box.

Consonant Sounds: W, C

The word <u>wagon</u> begins with the sound of <u>w</u>. Say the name of the picture in each box. If the name begins with the sound of <u>w</u>, print <u>W</u> on the line in the box.

1.	W	2.	_ _ _	3.	_ _ _
4.		5.	_ _ _	6.	_ _ _
7.	_ _ _	8.	_ _ _	9.	_ _ _
10.	_ _ _	11.	_ _ _	12.	_ _ _
13.	_ _ _	14.	_ _ _	15.	_ _ _

The word <u>cake</u> begins with the sound of <u>c</u>. Say the name of the picture in each box. If the name begins with the sound of <u>c</u>, print <u>C</u> on the line in the box.

1.	C	2.	_ _ _	3.	_ _ _
4.	_ _ _	5.	_ _ _	6.	_ _ _
7.	_ _ _	8.	_ _ _	9.	_ _ _
10.	_ _ _	11.	_ _ _	12.	_ _ _
13.	_ _ _	14.	_ _ _	15.	_ _ _

Consonant Sound: R

The word <u>rabbit</u> begins with the sound of <u>r</u>. Say the name of the picture in each box. If the name begins with the sound of <u>r</u>, print R on the line in the box.

1. R	2.	3.
4.	5.	6.
7.	8.	9.
10.	11.	12.
13.	14.	15.

The word <u>deer</u> ends with the sound of <u>r</u>. Say the name of the picture in each box. If the name ends with the sound of <u>r</u>, print <u>r</u> on the line in the box.

1. r	2.	3.
4.	5.	6.
7.	8.	9.
10.	11.	12.
13.	14.	15.

Consonant Sound: P

The word <u>pig</u> begins with the sound of <u>p</u>. Say the name of the picture in each box. If the name begins with the sound of <u>p</u>, print <u>P</u> on the line in the box.

1. P	2.	3.
4.	5.	6.
7.	8.	9.
10.	11.	12.
13.	14.	15.

The word <u>cap</u> ends with the sound of <u>p</u>. Say the name of the picture in each box. If the name ends with the sound of <u>p</u>, print <u>p</u> on the line in the box.

1. p	2.	3.
4.	5.	6.
7.	8.	9.
10.	11.	12.
13.	14.	15.

Consonant Sounds: C, N, P, R, W

Play Tic-Tac-Toe. Draw a line through the three pictures in a row that begin with the same sound. You may find more than one row in a game.

Consonant Sound: V

The word <u>valentine</u> begins with the sound of <u>v</u>. Say the name of the picture in each box. If the name begins with the sound of <u>v</u>, print <u>V</u> on the line in the box.

1. V	2.	3.
4.	5.	6.
7.	8.	9.
10.	11.	12.
13.	14.	15.

The word <u>cave</u> ends with the sound of <u>v</u>. Say the name of the picture in each box. If the name ends with the sound of <u>v</u>, print <u>v</u> on the line in the box.

1. v	2.	3.
4.	5.	6.
7.	8.	9.
10.	11.	12.
13.	14.	15.

Consonant Sounds: Qu, X, Y, Z

The word <u>queen</u> begins with the sound of <u>qu</u>. Say the name of the picture in each box. If the name begins with the sound of <u>qu</u>, print Qu on the line in the box.

1. Qu	2.	3.
4.	5.	6.

The word <u>ax</u> ends with the sound of <u>x</u>. Say the name of the picture in each box. If the name ends with the sound of <u>x</u>, print x on the line in the box.

1. X	2.	3.
4.	5.	6.

The word <u>yard</u> begins with the sound of <u>y</u>. Say the name of the picture in each box. If the name begins with the sound of <u>y</u>, print Y on the line in the box.

1. Y	2.	3.
4.	5.	6.

The word <u>zebra</u> begins with the sound of <u>z</u>. Say the name of the picture in each box. If the name begins with the sound of <u>z</u>, print Z on the line in the box.

1. Z	2.	3.
4.	5.	6.

Consonant Sounds: Qu, V, X, Y, Z

Say the name of the picture in each box. Print the letters of the beginning and ending sounds on the lines under each picture.

1. f x
2.
3.
4.
5.
6.
7.
8.
9.
10.
11.
12.

Short Vowel Sound: A

Say the name of the picture in each box. If the name has the short sound of <u>a</u>, print <u>a</u> on the line in the box.

1.	2.	3.
4.	5.	6.
7.	8.	9.
10.	11.	12.
13.	14.	15.

The word <u>jam</u> has the short sound of the vowel <u>a</u>. Say the name of the picture in each box. If the name has the short sound of <u>a</u>, circle the picture.

1.	2.	3.	4.
5.	6.	7.	8.
9.	10.	11.	12.
13.	14.	15.	16.
17.	18.	19.	20.

Short Vowel Rule

If a word has only one vowel, and it comes at the beginning or between two consonants, the vowel usually has a short sound.

Say the name of the picture in each box. Circle its name.

1.	2.	3.
cat cab pack (cap)	bat dam bag fan	mat man map can

4.	5.	6.
bad bag bat back	ax tax tag tam	cat cast man can

7.	8.	9.
cat cab cap tack	pass pan pat nap	sat cat rat ran

10.	11.	12.
tap tag tax bag	mad map dam nap	hand land fan tan

13.	14.	15.
tags tacks taps jacks	lap lamp land lad	ham has had hand

Short Vowel Sound: A

Say the name of each picture. Print the ending consonant of its name on the line.

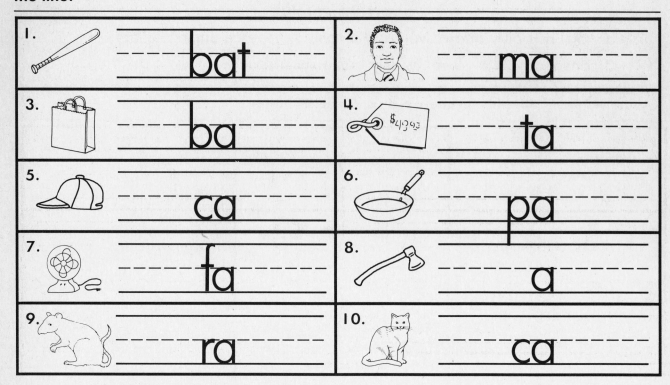

Say the name of each picture. Print the beginning and ending consonants of its name on the line.

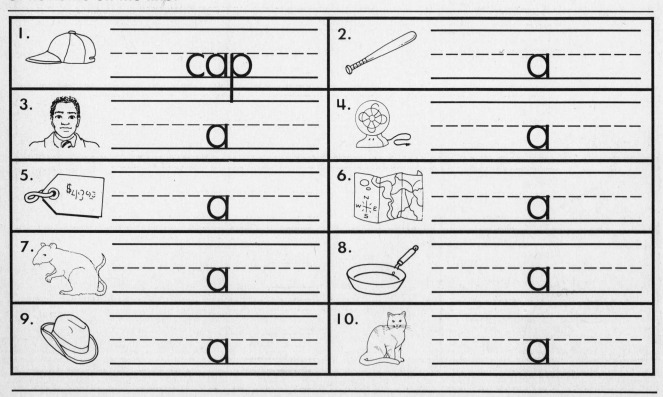

Short Vowel Sound: A

Say the name of each picture. Print its name on the line.

1. ax	2.
3.	4.
5.	6.
7.	8.
9.	10.

Read the words that are part of each sentence. Finish the sentence by writing the words from the box in the correct order on the line.

1. Sam has a bad cat .	a cat bad
2. At last Pat _____ .	Pam can tag
3. Dan can _____ .	maps pass the
4. The rat ran as fast _____ .	cat as the
5. Nan can hand _____ .	the tacks Dad

Short Vowel Sound: I

Say the name of the picture in each box. If the name has the short sound of i, print i on the line in the box.

1. i	2.	3.
4.	5.	6.
7.	8.	9.
10.	11.	12.
13.	14.	15.

The word hill has the short sound of the vowel i. Say the name of the picture in each box. If the name has the short sound of i, circle the picture.

1.	2.	3.	4.
5.	6.	7.	8.
9.	10.	11.	12.
13.	14.	15.	16.
17.	18.	19.	20.

Short Vowel Sound: I

Short Vowel Rule

If a word has only one vowel, and it comes at the beginning or between two consonants, the vowel usually has a short sound.

Say the name of the picture in each box. Circle its name.

1. big (bib) bit bat	2. pan nip pin nap	3. six sis ax wax
4. map nap wag wig	5. lid lad tip tap	6. fist fast list last
7. laps lips pill pins	8. dill hit bill hill	9. big bit bag bat
10. sing sang sink sank	11. pin pill pad pan	12. tip milk mat mitt
13. rang ring gas gang	14. pan pin pig gap	15. ring wig win wing

Short Vowel Sound: I

Say the name of each picture. Print the missing vowel on the line.

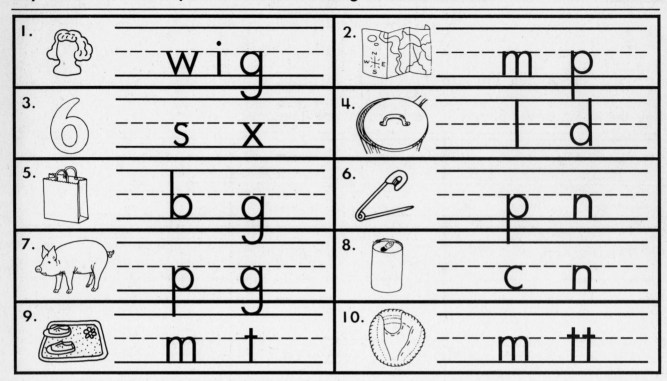

1. w i g
2. m __ p
3. s __ x
4. l __ d
5. b __ g
6. p __ n
7. p __ g
8. c __ n
9. m __ t
10. m __ tt

Say the name of each picture. Print the beginning and ending consonants of its name on the line.

1. b i b
2. __ i __
3. __ i __
4. __ i __
5. __ a __
6. __ i __
7. __ a __
8. __ i __
9. __ i __
10. __ a __

Say the name of each picture. Print its name on the line.

1. pig	2.
3.	4.
5.	6.
7.	8.
9.	10.

Read the words that are part of each sentence. Finish the sentence by writing the words from the box in the correct order on the line.

1. Dick bit his lip .	bit his lip
2. Kim will .	win jacks at
3. Hand the list .	the to man
4. Tim hid his bat .	sand in the
5. The six cats hid .	hats six the

Short Vowel Sound: U

Say the name of the picture in each box. If the name has the short sound of <u>u</u>, print <u>u</u> on the line in the box.

1. _____ u _____	2. _____	3. _____
4. _____	5. _____	6. _____
7. _____	8. _____	9. _____
10. _____	11. _____	12. _____
13. _____	14. _____	15. _____

The word <u>nuts</u> has the short sound of the vowel <u>u</u>. Say the name of the picture in each box. If the name has the short sound of <u>u</u>, circle the picture.

1.	2.	3.	4.
5.	6.	7.	8.
9.	10.	11.	12.
13.	14.	15.	16.
17.	18.	19.	20.

Short Vowel Rule

If a word has only one vowel, and it comes at the beginning or between two consonants, the vowel usually has a short sound.

Say the name of the picture in each box. Circle its name.

1.	bag	2.	pup	3.	mad
	(bug)		pin		damp
	big		pump		map
	dug		pass		dim

4.	muss	5.	gag	6.	bad
	miss		dug		bud
	sum		jug		bid
	sun		jog		dab

7.	gun	8.	hit	9.	cup
	gum		lid		cap
	mug		hid		cub
	mud		hill		cut

10.	tab	11.	tin	12.	sub
	bat		nut		bin
	tub		mitt		bun
	but		mat		bus

13.	mat	14.	dad	15.	cup
	meat		did		cap
	mitt		duck		cut
	tub		dust		cuff

Short Vowel Sound: U

Say the name of each picture. Print the missing vowel on the line.

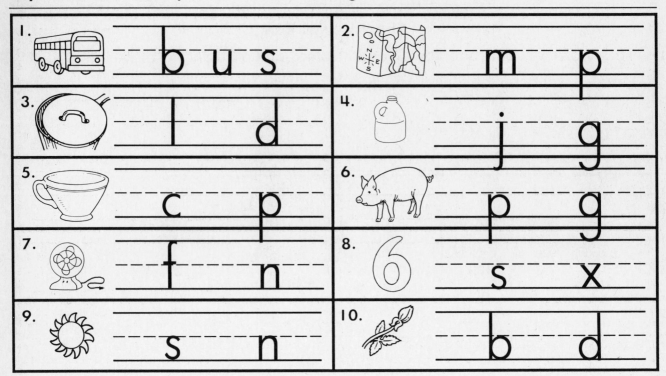

1. b u s
2. m ___ p
3. ___ l d
4. j ___ g
5. c ___ p
6. p ___ g
7. f ___ n
8. s ___ x
9. s ___ n
10. b ___ d

Say the name of each picture. Print the beginning and ending consonants of its name on the line.

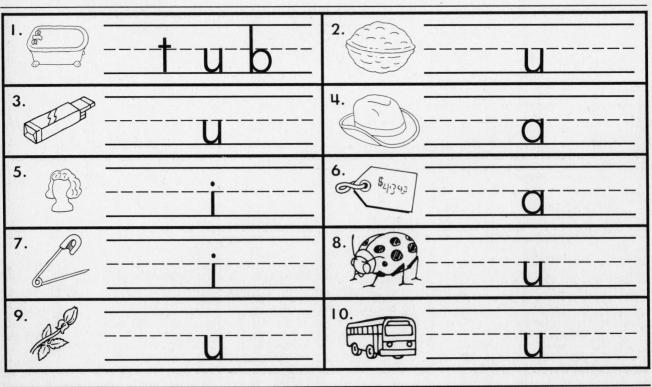

1. t u b
2. ___ u ___
3. ___ u ___
4. ___ a ___
5. ___ i ___
6. ___ a ___
7. ___ i ___
8. ___ u ___
9. ___ u ___
10. ___ u ___

Short Vowel Sound: U

Say the name of each picture. Print its name on the line.

1. bud	2.
3.	4.
5.	6.
7.	8.
9.	10.

Read the words that are part of a sentence. Finish the sentence by writing the words from the box in the correct order on the line.

1. Jack has a fat duck .	a fat duck
2. The big jug is .	milk of full
3. Can Bud ?	ham cut the
4. The tub is .	full suds of
5. Jan can run the pump .	the camp at

Short Vowel Sound: O

Say the name of the picture in each box. If the name has the short sound
of <u>o</u>, print <u>o</u> on the line in the box.

1. O	2.	3.
4.	5.	6.
7.	8.	9.
10.	11.	12.
13.	14.	15.

The word <u>pot</u> has the short sound of the vowel <u>o</u>. Say the name of the
picture in each box. If the name has the short sound of <u>o</u>, circle the picture.

1.	2.	3.	4.
5.	6.	7.	8.
9.	10.	11.	12.
13.	14.	15.	16.
17.	18.	19.	20.

Short Vowel Sound: O

Short Vowel Rule

If a word has only one vowel, and it comes at the beginning or between two consonants, the vowel usually has a short sound.

Say the name of the picture in each box. Circle its name.

1.	2.	3.
fix (box) ox bat	cot cut cat cod	gap pig pup pop

4.	5.	6.
us as ox ax	pat pit pot top	rug dig rag rat

7.	8.	9.
mud pan map mop	box fox fix six	tap top pot pat

10.	11.	12.
cat tot cot pup	rug rag rod rid	lock lack lick luck

13.	14.	15.
sack sock sick suck	dot hill doll dill	rods dots rack rock

Short Vowel Sound: O

Say the name of each picture. Print the missing vowel on the line.

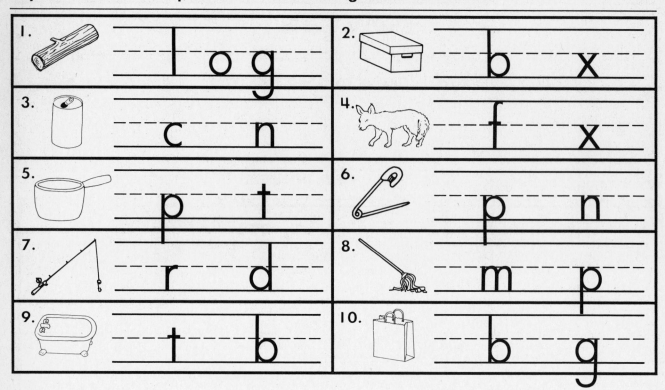

1. l o g
2. b o x
3. c o n
4. f o x
5. p o t
6. p o n
7. r o d
8. m o p
9. t o b
10. b o g

Say the name of each picture. Print the beginning and ending consonants of its name on the line.

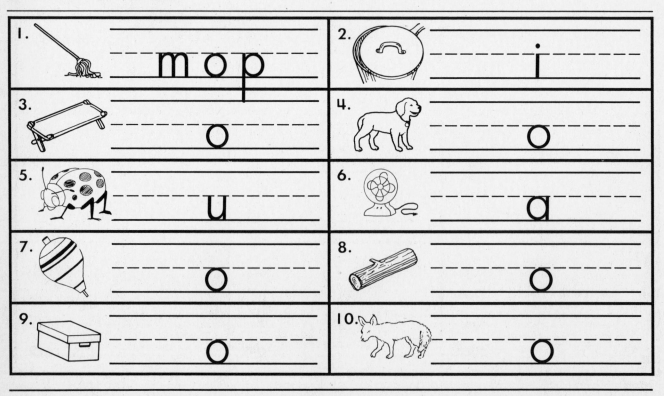

1. m o p
2. __ i __
3. __ o __
4. __ o __
5. __ u __
6. __ a __
7. __ o __
8. __ o __
9. __ o __
10. __ o __

Short Vowel Sound: O

Say the name of each picture. Print its name on the line.

1.	top	2.	
3.		4.	
5.		6.	
7.		8.	
9.		10.	

Read the words that are part of a sentence. Finish the sentence by writing the words from the box in the correct order on the line.

1. Tod will	fix the mop .	the fix mop
2. The dog has spots	.	its back on
3. Dot has a doll, but	.	lost it is
4. Bob will toss the box	.	the cot on
5. Polly will rub the moss	.	off the rock

Short Vowel Sound: E

Say the name of the picture in each box. If the name has the short sound of e, print e on the line in the box.

1. ___e___	2. _____	3. _____
4. _____	5. _____	6. _____
7. _____	8. _____	9. _____
10. _____	11. _____	12. _____
13. _____	14. _____	15. _____

The word net has the short sound of the vowel e. Say the name of the picture in each box. If the name has the short sound of e, circle the picture.

1.	2.	3.	4.
5.	6.	7.	8.
9.	10.	11.	12.
13.	14.	15.	16.
17.	18.	19.	20.

Short Vowel Sound: E

Short Vowel Rule

If a word has only one vowel, and it comes at the beginning or between two consonants, the vowel usually has a short sound.

Say the name of the picture in each box. Circle its name.

1. (bed) bad bud bid	2. nap pin pan pen	3. ten net nut not
4. tan test ten tin	5. hem hen hum him	6. met net men man
7. egg bag beg big	8. jut just jot jet	9. win web bet wag
10. six nuts nest tots	11. will well win wall	12. desk dip dock disk
13. bat bet bill bell	14. tint nest tent tot	15. vat vast west vest

Short Vowel Sound: E

Say the name of each picture. Print the missing vowel on the line.

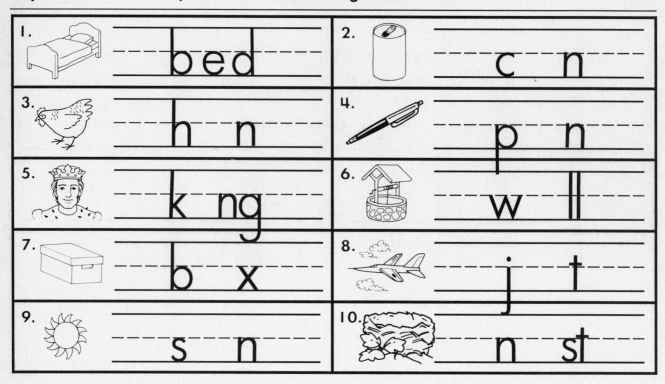

1. b e d
2. c _ n
3. h _ n
4. p _ n
5. k _ ng
6. w _ ll
7. b _ x
8. j _ t
9. s _ n
10. n _ st

Say the name of each picture. Print the beginning and ending consonants of its name on the line.

1. t e n
2. _ i _
3. _ e _
4. _ e _
5. _ a _
6. _ e _
7. _ e _
8. _ e _
9. _ e _
10. _ i _

Short Vowel Sound: E

43

Say the name of each picture. Print its name on the line.

1. hen
2.
3.
4.
5.
6.
7.
8.
9.
10.

Read the words that are part of each sentence. Finish the sentence by writing the words from the box in the correct order on the line.

1. Ned fell and cut his leg . | leg cut his
2. Ted fed . | hen pet his
3. Ben will lend the . | to pen Nell
4. Bess and Tess can . | pass test the
5. Let us send a . | Ted gift to

Short Vowel Compound Words

A **compound word** is a word made up of two or more words. Circle the words within each compound word below.

1. (dust)(pan)	2. pigpen	3. sunset
4. upset	5. windmill	6. bathtub
7. cannot	8. uphill	9. sandbox
10. padlock	11. handbag	12. airplane
13. himself	14. handcuffs	15. football

Read the words that are part of each sentence. Then circle the word in the box that will finish the sentence. Print the word on the line.

1. Jack fed the pigs in the _____pigpen_____ .	padlock (pigpen) dustpan
2. Bob will get _____ a pet.	handcuffs handbag himself
3. The gate has a _____ .	padlock pigpen windmill
4. Janet will fill up the _____ .	uphill upset bathtub
5. Jill lost a _____ in the bank.	sunset sandbox handbag

Short Vowel Compound Words

Form a compound word by drawing a line from each word in the first list to a word in the second list. Then print the word on the line beside its picture.

air	mill
foot	plane
bath	ball
wind	tub

1. airplane

2.

3.

4.

pad	box
hand	pan
sand	lock
dust	cuffs

1.

2.

3.

4.

Two-Syllable Words

Say the name of the picture in each box. Listen for the beginning, middle, and ending consonant sounds in the name. Print the letters of the beginning, middle, and ending sounds on the correct line below the picture.

1.	2.	3.
r b t		

4.	5.	6.

7.	8.	9.

10.	11.	12.

Long Vowel Sound: A

Say the name of the picture in each box. If the name has the long sound of <u>a</u>, print <u>a</u> on the line in the box.

1. a	2.	3.
4.	5.	6.
7.	8.	9.
10.	11.	12.
13.	14.	15.

The word <u>rake</u> has the long sound of the vowel <u>a</u>. Say the name of each picture. If the name has the long sound of <u>a</u>, circle the picture.

1.	2.	3.	4.
5.	6.	7.	8.
9.	10.	11.	12.
13.	14.	15.	16.
17.	18.	19.	20.

Long Vowel Sound: A

Long Vowel Rule I

If a word with one syllable has two vowels, the first vowel usually has a long sound and the second vowel is silent.

Say the name of the picture in each box. Circle its name.

#		Words
1.		cap / cape / sake / **cake**
2.		tap / tape / pale / top
3.		lick / lack / lake / lock
4.		safe / sake / sale / sail
5.		game / gave / gate / gale
6.		vase / save / vane / van
7.		gave / game / gate / gain
8.		came / gain / can / cane
9.		cap / map / cape / ape
10.		made / mad / mail / nail
11.		rack / rake / rock / rain
12.		made / lame / mail / nail
13.		sail / sill / safe / sad
14.		cat / cot / cave / cape
15.		rave / run / ran / rain

Long Vowel Sound: A

Say the name of each picture. Print the missing vowel on the line.

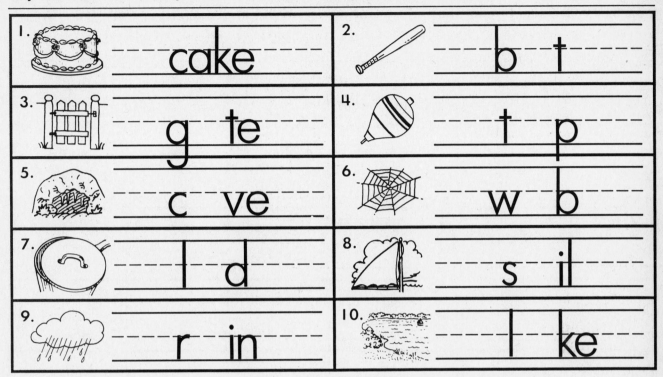

1. cake
2. b t
3. g te
4. t p
5. c ve
6. w b
7. l d
8. s il
9. r in
10. l ke

Say the name of each picture. Print its name on the line.

1. tape
2.
3.
4.
5.
6.
7.
8.
9.
10.

Long Vowel Sound: A

Read the words that are part of each sentence. Then circle the word in the box that will finish the sentence. Print the word on the line.

1. Dad has red _paint_ in the can.	pant (paint) paid
2. Jane went to the _____ in the rain.	game cane gap
3. The _____ fell upon the land.	made rain ran
4. I will _____ a date and nut cake.	back rake bake
5. We got a pail and a _____ at the sale.	ran rain rake
6. A cub is in the _____ .	gave cave cap
7. Dave will _____ in the lake.	rack paint wade
8. Ann has _____ a red cape.	made mad wade
9. We _____ cake at the picnic.	hate at ate
10. Can the puppet _____ to us?	wake vase wave
11. We fed the _____ to Jake.	cake cave gate

Long Vowel Sound: I

Say the name of the picture in each box. If the name has the long sound of i, print i on the line in the box.

1.	2.	3.
4.	5.	6.
7.	8.	9.
10.	11.	12.
13.	14.	15.

The word knife has the long sound of the vowel i. Say the name of the picture in each box. If the name has the long sound of i, circle the picture.

1.	2.	3.	4.
5.	6.	7.	8.
9.	10.	11.	12.
13.	14.	15.	16.
17.	18.	19.	20.

Long Vowel Rule I

If a word with one syllable has two vowels, the first vowel usually has a long sound and the second vowel is silent.

Say the name of the picture in each box. Circle its name.

1.	pin	2.	kit	3.	nine
	(pie)		cat		mine
	pit		bite		Nan
	pine		kite		man

4.	sit	5.	van	6.	pin
	sip		vine		dive
	six		fin		pipe
	size		vane		pine

7.	pipe	8.	live	9.	five
	dine		lift		fit
	pin		hive		fine
	pine		hid		fin

10.	five	11.	file	12.	red
	fire		hail		ripe
	fine		pill		ride
	fin		hill		rid

13.	tire	14.	back	15.	dim
	fire		bit		tie
	time		bike		dime
	tin		kite		dive

Long Vowel Sound: I

Say the name of each picture. Print the missing vowel on the line.

1.	p i e	2.	c _ t
3.	n _ ne	4.	f _ re
5.	h _ n	6.	h _ ll
7.	f _ ve	8.	r _ de
9.	p _ n	10.	p _ ne

Say the name of each picture. Print its name on the line.

1.	vine	2.	
3.		4.	
5.		6.	
7.		8.	
9.		10.	

Long Vowel Sound: I

Read the words that are part of each sentence. Then circle the word in the box that will finish the sentence. Print the word on the line.

1. Jim can hike for five **miles** .	mills mines (miles)
2. Mike will get himself a _____ .	hike bike back
3. Dad can _____ Kate to rake.	hire hid tire
4. Kim will _____ into the lake.	dine dive hid
5. It is not wise to tell a _____ .	lie tie lip
6. A dog can save your _____ .	like lift life
7. The left _____ of the cab has a dent.	mile sad side
8. It is _____ to ride to the game.	tire Tim time
9. _____ the dog to the gate.	Ted Tie Tim
10. Jane will take a _____ on a bus.	hide ride rid
11. Pedro likes _____ melons.	rip pipe ripe

Say the name of the picture in each box. If the name has the long sound of u, print u on the line in the box.

1. ___u___	2. ___	3. ___
4. ___	5. ___	6. ___
7. ___	8. ___	9. ___
10. ___	11. ___	12. ___
13. ___	14. ___	15. ___

The word cube has the long sound of the vowel u. Say the name of the picture in each box. If the name has the long sound of u, circle the picture.

1.	2.	3.	4.
5.	6.	7.	8.
9.	10.	11.	12.
13.	14.	15.	16.
17.	18.	19.	20.

Long Vowel Sound: U

Long Vowel Rule I

If a word with one syllable has two vowels, the first vowel usually has a long sound and the second vowel is silent.

Long Vowel Rule II

If a word (or syllable) has only one vowel and it comes at the end of the word (or syllable), the vowel is usually long.

Say the name of each picture. Circle its name.

1. cube / cub / cute / cut	2. time / fin / tune / tin	3. rug / ruler / rid / ride
4. tone / tub / tug / tube	5. Joan / June / Jack / Jim	6. male / mill / mule / mug
7. fun / fan / flute / fake	8. sat / suit / seat / sun	9. jam / jug / June / juice
10. flute / fruit / rug / fin	11. tune / sun / up / unicorn	12. uniform / unit / man / rug
13. tub / tune / tell / tulip	14. nose / cut / cupid / cute	15. dog / dome / dot / dune

Long Vowel Sound: U

Say the name of each picture. Print the missing vowel on the line.

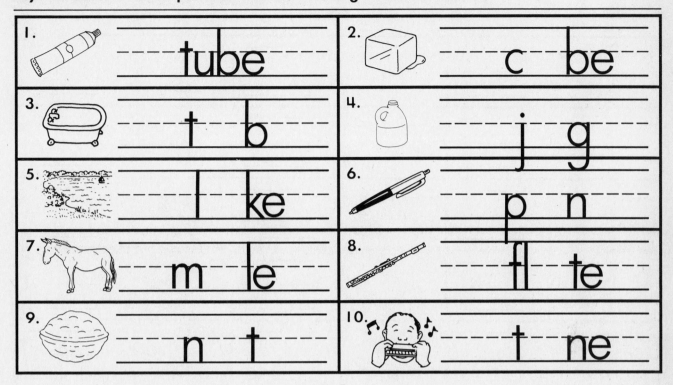

1. tube
2. c_be
3. t_b
4. j_g
5. l_ke
6. p_n
7. m_le
8. fl_te
9. n_t
10. t_ne

Say the name of each picture. Print its name on the line.

1. flute
2.
3.
4.
5.
6.
7.
8.
9.
10.

Long Vowel Sound: O

Say the name of the picture in each box. If the name has the long sound
of o, print o on the line in the box.

1. ___ **O**	2. ___	3. ___
4. ___	5. ___	6. ___
7. ___	8. ___	9. ___
10. ___	11. ___	12. ___
13. ___	14. ___	15. ___

The word boat has the long sound of the vowel o. Say the name of each
picture. If the name has the long sound of o, circle the picture.

1.	2.	3.	4.
5.	6.	7.	8.
9.	10.	11.	12.
13.	14.	15.	16.
17.	18.	19.	20.

Long Vowel Rule I

If a word with one syllable has two vowels, the first vowel usually has a long sound and the second vowel is silent.

Long Vowel Rule II

If a word (or syllable) has only one vowel and it comes at the end of the word (or syllable), the vowel is usually long.

Say the name of each picture. Circle its name.

1. (rope) rip robe rib	2. dot top toe toad	3. bun bone not note
4. dime dig dim dome	5. cane cone nose can	6. home hop hoe hope
7. nod no nose hose	8. got goat go goal	9. hot ham home hose
10. rod road red dose	11. bite bait bat boat	12. toad tube top dot
13. cat cute cot coat	14. road rod rose nose	15. rob ripe rib robe

Long Vowel Sound: O

Say the name of each picture. Print the missing vowel on the line.

1.	h o e	2.	c _ ne
3.	n _ se	4.	b _ x
5.	d _ me	6.	d _ ve
7.	t _ ad	8.	c _ b
9.	r _ d	10.	r _ ad

Say the name of each picture. Print its name on the line.

1.	rope	2.	
3.		4.	
5.		6.	
7.		8.	
9.		10.	

Read the words that are part of each sentence. Then circle the word in the box that will finish the sentence. Print the word on the line.

1. Don tied the goat with a ___rope___ .	(rope) rip rode
2. Do you like to ride in a _____ ?	bat boat goat
3. Mom sent a _____ to me.	got note goat
4. Pam can tell us lots of _____ .	jacks jokes packs
5. Jan _____ the bike up the hill.	rod road rode
6. The cab ran off the _____ and had to stop.	rod road rose
7. The _____ can hop up on the rock.	toad Tod dome
8. Tom fell and got a bump on his _____ .	note not nose
9. It is fun to _____ in a tub of soap suds.	sock soak sack
10. The dog will dig a hole to hide the _____ .	cot boat bone
11. Luke has a red _____ .	coat go joke

Say the name of the picture in each box. If the name has the long sound of e, print e on the line in the box.

1. e	2.	3.
4.	5.	6.
7.	8.	9.
10.	11.	12.
13.	14.	15.

The word bee has the long sound of the vowel e. Say the name of each picture. If the name has the long sound of e, circle the picture.

1.	2.	3.	4.
5.	6.	7.	8.
9.	10.	11.	12.
13.	14.	15.	16.
17.	18.	19.	20.

Long Vowel Sound: E

Long Vowel Rule I

If a word with one syllable has two vowels, the first vowel usually has a long sound and the second vowel is silent.

Long Vowel Rule II

If a word (or syllable) has only one vowel and it comes at the end of the word (or syllable), the vowel is usually long.

Say the name of the picture in each box. Circle its name.

1.	left / (leaf) / lead / feel	2.	beet / best / bee / bet	3.	backs / beaks / beds / beads
4.	feet / feel / fat / fed	5.	hill / hit / heel / he	6.	met / meat / me / team
7.	teas / sent / set / seat	8.	jet / jell / peep / jeep	9.	bite / beet / bee / bet
10.	quick / quilt / queen / need	11.	web / weed / weak / wade	12.	pens / pans / peas / pies
13.	ten / tea / tag / teeth	14.	seal / sea / sail / sell	15.	bones / bends / bins / beans

Long Vowel Sound: E

Say the name of each picture. Print the missing vowel on the line.

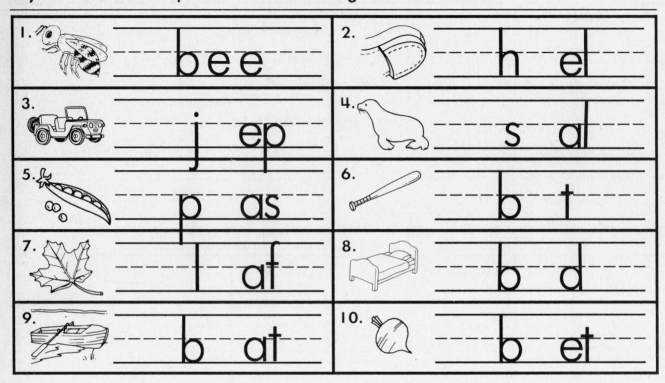

1. b e e
2. h e l
3. j ep
4. s al
5. p as
6. b t
7. l af
8. b d
9. b at
10. b et

Say the name of each picture. Print its name on the line.

1. seat
2.
3.
4.
5.
6.
7.
8.
9.
10.

Long Vowel Sound: E

Read the words that are part of each sentence. Finish the sentence by writing the words from the box in the correct order on the line.

1. Jean needs nine kids _for the team_ .	the team for
2. The sick man _____ .	weak quite feels
3. Eve likes _____ .	beets to eat
4. Tom will not keep his feet _____ .	the off seat
5. You keep _____ .	desk neat your
6. Pete will go to the _____ .	week next sea
7. Do you feed _____ ?	dog meat your
8. We took the jeep _____ .	to get meat
9. Hot dogs and beans make _____ .	a meal fun
10. Lee Ann will sit on _____ .	red seat the
11. Dee will have tea with _____ .	home at me

Long Vowel Compound Words

A **compound word** is a word made up of two or more words. Circle the words within each compound word.

1. (bee)(hive)	2. beside	3. homemade
4. oatmeal	5. toenail	6. fireside
7. seaweed	8. raincoat	9. mealtime
10. nickname	11. teapot	12. pipeline
13. lifeboat	14. railroad	15. teammate

Read the words that are part of each sentence. Then circle the word in the box that will finish the sentence. Print the word on the line.

1. Is Tad your nickname ?	napkin nineteen (nickname)
2. Did you upset the _____ ?	beehive beside homemade
3. Jean likes to eat _____ .	mealtime oatmeal fireside
4. His dad gave him a ride in a _____ .	railroad sailboat pipeline
5. Tom is a _____ of Jean and Pete.	teammate mealtime homemade

Compound and Two-Syllable Words

In each part, draw a line from each word in the first list to a word in the second list to make a compound or two-syllable word. Print the word on the line beside its picture.

tea   boat

bee   coat

rain   hive

sail   pot

1. teapot

2.

3.

4.

six   box

pea   pole

sand   teen

tad   nut

1.

2.

3.

4.

Two-Syllable Words

Say the name of the picture in each box. Listen for the vowel sounds in the name. Print the vowels on the correct line below the picture.

1.	2.	3.	4.
e u			

5.	6.	7.	8.

9.	10.	11.	12.

13.	14.	15.	16.

The name of each picture begins with the sound of the blend <u>br</u>, <u>cr</u>, <u>dr</u>, or <u>fr</u>. Say the picture's name. Listen for the beginning sound of the name. Print the beginning blend on the line in the box.

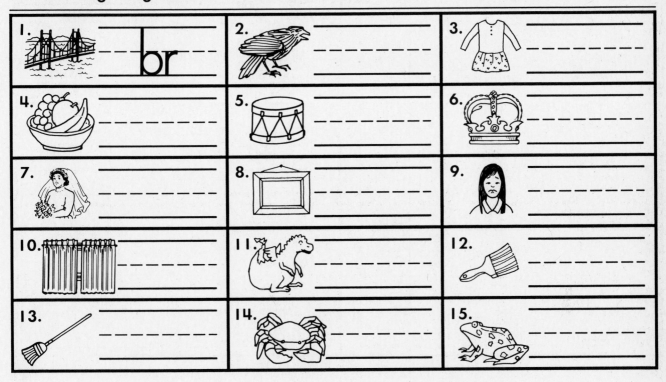

The name of each picture begins with the sound of the blend <u>gr</u>, <u>pr</u>, or <u>tr</u>. Say the picture's name. Listen for the beginning sound of the name. Print the beginning blend on the line in the box.

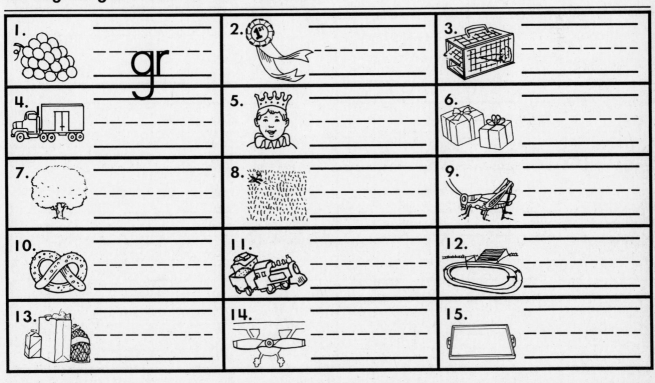

R Blends

Say the name of each picture. Draw a line from the picture to its name.

1.	braid	
	bride	
	brick	
	bridge	
2.	crow	
	grapes	
	grass	
	crab	
3.	dress	
	dragon	
	drum	
	drapes	
4.	tree	
	trap	
	truck	
	train	
5.	fruit	
	prize	
	frog	
	frame	
6.	tray	
	broom	
	trunk	
	track	

Say the name of each picture. Print its name on the line.

1. prize

2. _____

3. _____

4. _____

5. _____

6. _____

7. _____

8. _____

R Blends

Read the words that are part of each sentence. Then circle the word in the box that will finish the sentence. Print the word on the line.

1. Eve likes to win ____prizes____ .	press (prizes) grass
2. The dog will _____ from the creek.	dream drink track
3. Sue _____ the cub from the trap.	fried freed trade
4. I will _____ bikes with you.	trade drain trap
5. Give me the tube of hand_____ near the sink.	crib cream dream
6. My train fell off the track and _____ .	broke croak braid
7. _____ your name inside your coat.	Prize Trip Print
8. Use care if you _____ the road.	press cross grass
9. Dad will bring gifts back from his _____ .	trap trip drip
10. The ants made a trail to the _____ in the tree.	trick track crack
11. The _____ jumped away.	brick frog from

L Blends

Say the name of the picture in each box. If the name begins with the sound of <u>cl</u> or <u>pl</u>, print <u>cl</u> or <u>pl</u> on the line.

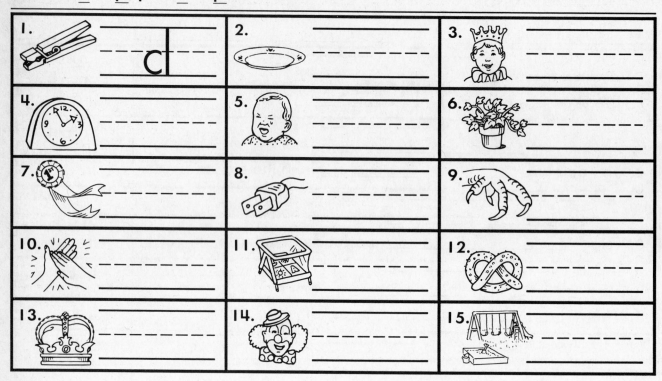

Say the name of the picture in each box. If the name begins with the sound of <u>bl</u>, <u>fl</u>, or <u>gl</u>, print <u>bl</u>, <u>fl</u>, or <u>gl</u> on the line.

Say the name of each picture. Circle its name.

1.	clock black **block**	2.	flag flap frog	3.	glad globe grade
4.	clip clap flap	5.	blade pleat plate	6.	from flat float
7.	class gloss glass	8.	clock click block	9.	freed fleet float
10.	bleed blade bride	11.	plus frog plug	12.	fly ply float
13.	glue blue clue	14.	print plan plant	15.	plant black blanket

Say the name of each picture. Print its name on the line.

1. flat

2.

3.

4.

5.

6.

7.

8.

9.

10.

L Blends

Read the words that are part of each sentence. Then circle the word in the box that will finish the sentence. Print the word on the line.

1. We will _plan_ a class picnic.	glass plus (plan)
2. Bring a glass and a _____ with you.	blend plate flat
3. Please _____ if Glen sings.	clip clap glad
4. Clem has _____ hair.	blond brand blade
5. Jean fed grain to the _____ of ducks.	block black flock
6. Did you _____ the tree near the drive?	bland plank plant
7. Please drink your _____ of milk.	class glass brass
8. The yellow cat plays with the _____ dog.	block black brick
9. Tom hung the _____ at the top of the pole.	plot flame flag
10. Brad and Fran are in the same _____.	class grass brass
11. Don't _____ on the ice.	slim slam slip

S Blends

All the two-letter s blends are shown below. Say the name of each picture. Listen for the beginning blend. Print the letters of the beginning blend on the line in the box.   sc   sk   sl   sm   sn   sp   st   sw

All the three-letter s blends are shown below. Say the name of each picture. Listen for the beginning blend. Print the letters of the beginning blend on the line in the box.   scr   spl   spr   squ   str

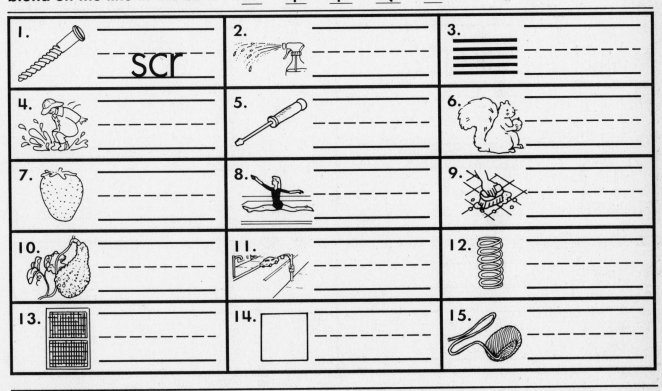

S Blends

Say the name of the picture in each box. Circle its name.

1.	still / spell / (spill)	2.	slump / stamp / stripe	3.	screen / stream / scale
4.	spring / string / sling	5.	skunk / spell / skip	6.	sting / sling / swing
7.	snake / skate / sake	8.	skid / slide / stride	9.	spoke / smoke / snack
10.	scream / spring / spray	11.	square / scrub / skate	12.	swell / scold / stole
13.	split / spot / slot	14.	stub / scab / scrub	15.	sling / swing / spring

Say the name of the picture in each box. Print its name on the line.

1.	skate	2.	
3.		4.	
5.		6.	
7.		8.	
9.		10.	

S Blends

Read the words that are part of each sentence. Finish the sentence by writing the words from the box in the correct order on the line.

1. The cat likes to _scare the dog_ .	the dog scare
2. Dad can _____.	mile a swim
3. Do you like to _____?	the smell tulips
4. Stan likes to go _____.	the stream to
5. The frog in the pond _____.	splash made a
6. Clean the spot _____.	your sleeve off
7. I help my father _____.	the floor scrub
8. Can you spin the top _____?	square in the
9. I can do tricks _____.	my on skates
10. Jim fell and _____.	toe sprained his
11. Green means go and _____.	means red stop

Y as a Vowel

1. When **y** is the only vowel at the end of a one-syllable word, it sounds like long **i**.
2. When **y** is at the end of a word with more than one syllable, it sounds like long **e**.

Read each word. Print it in the correct column.

by	lily	try	cry
happy	my	sky	baby
merry	funny	fry	dry
pony	fly	puppy	silly

Y has the long sound of **i**.	**Y** has the long sound of **e**.
by	happy

Y as a Vowel

Read each sentence. Circle the words in which y has the long sound of i.

1. (By) twelve o'clock the (sky) will be sunny.

2. Yes, Teddy, you may try to ride the pony.

3. The land in the valley is dry and sandy.

4. The jet will fly up to the sunny blue sky.

5. Tammy can try to ride my bike.

Read each sentence. Circle the words in which y has the long sound of e.

1. The shaggy puppy likes my sly cat.

2. Mary and Sally gave a lily to the pretty lady.

3. The happy baby did not cry.

4. Molly will lie on the dry sand to get a suntan.

5. The shiny penny fell into the well.

W as a Vowel

> 1. When **w** begins a word or syllable, it has a consonant sound, as in **wag**.
>
> 2. When **w** ends a word or syllable, it is a silent vowel, as in **grow**.

Read each word. Print it in the correct column.

wagon	wig	windmill	snow
glow	wind	blow	weeds
we	grow	bow	bowl
wag	slow	flow	watch

W has a consonant sound.	**W** is a silent vowel.
wagon	glow

Consonant Digraph: TH

The word <u>thumb</u> begins with the sound of <u>th</u>. Say the name of the picture in each box. If the name begins with the sound of <u>th</u>, print <u>th</u> in the box.

1. th	2.	3.
4.	5.	6.
7.	8.	9.
10.	11.	12.
13.	14.	15.
16.	17.	18.

The <u>th</u> in <u>thorn</u> and <u>bath</u> has a soft sound. The <u>th</u> in <u>that</u> and <u>bathe</u> has a hard sound. Say each word listed below. Circle the words in which <u>th</u> stands for a hard sound.

1.	2.	3.
thin	mother	those
thick	the	father
(them)	throne	thank
that	teeth	moth
cloth	then	three
clothes	themselves	this
path	bath	these
with	bathe	think

Consonant Digraph: WH

The word <u>wheel</u> begins with the sound of <u>wh</u>. Say the name of the picture in each box. If the name begins with the sound of <u>wh</u>, print <u>wh</u> in the box.

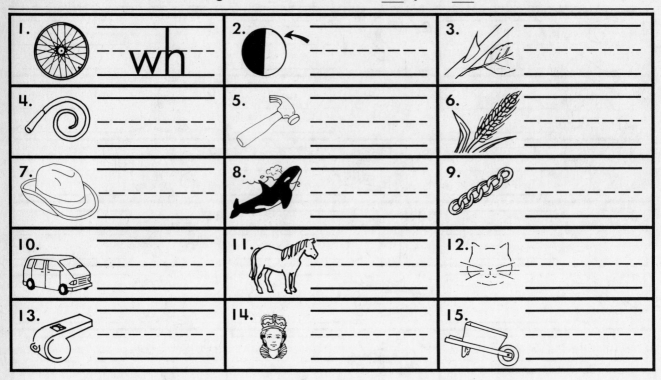

Play Tic-Tac-Toe. Draw a line through the three pictures in a row that begin with the same sound. You may find more than one row in a game.

Say the name of each picture. Draw a line from the picture to its name.

1.	throne thorn three thrush	2.	wheat whale white wheel
3.	well whisk whip whistle	4.	thick think thumb thin
5.	window mow wagon windmill	6.	teeth moth bath father

Read the words that are part of each sentence. Circle the word in the box that will finish the sentence. Print the word on the line.

1. That cloth is not ___white___ .	think (white) wheat
2. The white _____ sat on the window sill.	path moth bath
3. Why did the baby _____ his blocks away?	throne window throw
4. _____ the wheat is ripe, it is yellow.	When The Whip

Consonant Digraph: SH

The word <u>shell</u> begins with the sound of <u>sh</u>. Say the name of the picture in each box. If the name begins with the sound of <u>sh</u>, print <u>sh</u> on the line.

Say the name of the picture in each box. Circle its name.

1.	skip (ship) slip	2.	sheep sleep sheet	3.	desk dash dish
4.	spears shirt sheep	5.	shelf shell shall	6.	shade slide shape
7.	shelf shell shall	8.	blush thrush brush	9.	blush thrush brush
10.	wishbone fishbone fishbowl	11.	wishbone fishbone fishbowl	12.	fellow shallow shadow

Consonant Digraph: CH

The word <u>chair</u> begins with the sound of <u>ch</u>. Say the name of the picture in each box. If the name begins with the sound of <u>ch</u>, print <u>ch</u> in the box.

Say the name of each picture. Circle its name.

1.	chain (chin) shin	2.	chain chin shin	3.	sheep cheese cheer
4.	wrench watch bench	5.	hitch watch match	6.	checks chicks shakes
7.	cheese cheer shave	8.	path reach peach	9.	chip pitch patch
10.	club crutch crush	11.	shiny chipmunk chimney	12.	chimney chipmunk shipmate

Consonant Digraphs

Say the name of the picture in each box. Listen for a beginning, middle, or ending consonant digraph sound in the name. Print the letters of the digraph on the correct line below the picture.

1.	2.	3.
sh		

4.	5.	6.
		3

7.	8.	9.

10.	11.	12.

Consonant Digraphs

Read the words that are part of each sentence. Finish the sentence by writing the words from the box in the correct order on the line.

1.	Sue can mow the grass	while I rake .	I while rake
2.	The smoke from the	____ .	is white chimney
3.	The tree makes	____ .	a scary shadow
4.	I will tie a bow	____ .	sash the with
5.	That path to the	____ .	steep ranch is
6.	Tom fed chestnuts	____ .	the to chipmunk
7.	We will	____ .	wheat cut the
8.	Then we will	____ .	the sheep shear
9.	The baby was held	____ .	by father his
10.	Did you ever	____ ?	whale a see
11.	When did the children	____ ?	beach see the

Hard and Soft Sounds of C

When **c** is followed by **e**, **i**, or **y**, it usually has a soft sound, or the sound of **s**.

Say the name of the picture in each box. If the name has the soft sound of **c**, circle its name.

1. (celery)	2. cents	3. camel
4. car	5. pencil	6. mice
7. city	8. card	9. cymbals
10. face	11. clap	12. circle
13. fence	14. crow	15. circus

Hard and Soft Sounds of C

Say the name of the picture in each box. Circle its name.

1.	(city) coat kitty	2.	male mole mice	3.	fact face fame
4.	press prince price	5.	clock click cluck	6.	fancy since fence
7.	sky fry cry	8.	cans cents sands	9.	cow crow throw
10.	dime dice dose	11.	let us lemon lettuce	12.	camels cymbals canals
13.	pencil pens guns	14.	prince princess prices	15.	neckbone necktie necklace

Read the words that are part of each sentence. Circle the word in the box that will finish the sentence. Print the word on the line.

1. Ten _____ is the same as a dime.	(cents) sense sent
2. The _____ had three white mice as pets.	price print prince
3. _____ ate spice cake and ice cream.	Grade Grace Grate
4. We will trim the dress with _____ .	late mice lace
5. My class will go to the _____ .	circus since send

Hard and Soft Sounds of G

When **g** is followed by **e**, **i**, or **y**, it usually has a soft sound, or the sound of **j**.

Say the name of the picture in each box. If the name has the soft sound of **g**, circle its name.

1. (gem)	2. gym	3. grapes
4. vegetables	5. globe	6. cage
7. gate	8. stage	9. giraffe
10. flag	11. gingerbread	12. frog
13. bridge	14. wagon	15. geranium

Say the name of the picture in each box. Circle its name.

1.	cape (cage) cake	2.	gun gum pun	3.	gym gum gem
4.	wig wag wage	5.	stay stage step	6.	gain game gave
7.	gym gum gem	8.	gate got goat	9.	glide globe gloat
10.	glaze gloss glass	11.	grant giant grain	12.	brig bride bridge
13.	drop dragon drapes	14.	giraffe gruff grate	15.	golf jog frog

Read the words that are part of each sentence. Circle the word in the box that will finish the sentence. Print the word on the line.

1. What did the ____message____ say?

mittens
(message)
manage

2. What did Gus keep in the _____ ?

cage
cane
came

3. A _____ eats green leaves.

graft
giraffe
gruff

4. Why did Gary run across the _____ ?

fudge
page
bridge

5. Which _____ will the play be on?

rage
stage
stay

Soft Sounds of C and G

**Read each sentence. Underline the words in which <u>g</u> has a soft sound.
Then circle the words in which <u>c</u> has a soft sound.**

1. It is (nice) to sit by a (fireplace.)

2. The mice have lots of space in their nest.

3. A huge globe hung from the ceiling.

4. The bandits held up the stagecoach.

5. His father let him keep the change.

6. They will have ice cream and fruit juice at the dance.

7. Kim came with a strange message.

8. Soap helps us to get rid of germs.

9. Use your pencil to print your name and age on this tag.

10. Grace will lead the class in a pledge to the flag.

The word <u>arm</u> has the sound of <u>ar</u>. Say the name of the picture in each box. Print <u>ar</u> on the line in the box if you hear the sound of <u>ar</u>.

Say the name of the picture in each box. Circle its name.

1. Art / (art) / are
2. arm / are / air
3. spar / inch / arch
4. car / cab / card
5. card / carve / cart
6. dark / dart / darn
7. yarn / rats / tart
8. bend / bark / barn
9. jar / jam / Jim
10. stay / star / stare
11. yard / yarn / yellow
12. yard / yarn / rare
13. harp / hard / harm
14. spanks / sparks / spends
15. game / garbage / garden

AR

Read the words that are part of each rhyme. Choose the word from the box that will finish the rhyme. Print the word on the line.

1. Children from afar Are wishing on a —.	**star**	scare star stare
2. Can you see the charm In life on a —?		farm harm arm
3. Hark! Can you hear the bark Of dogs across the —?		lark dark park
4. On Tuesday we will start To make the goat a —.		chart cart part
5. On Friday we can place The goat cart in a —.		lace face race

Read the words that are part of each sentence. Finish the sentence by writing the words from the box in the correct order on the line.

1. Please, will you **darn my socks** ?		darn socks my
2. The spark set fire _____ .		the barn to
3. The wind blows _____ .		in hard March
4. Martin grows lettuce _____ .		garden in his
5. The dress will be stiff if _____ .		it starch we

The word <u>horn</u> has the sound of <u>or</u>. Say the name of the picture in each box. Print <u>or</u> on the line in the box if you hear the sound of <u>or</u>.

1. or	2.	3.
4.	5.	6.
7.	8.	9.
10.	11.	12.
13.	14.	15.

Say the name of the picture in each box. Circle its name.

1. (corn) car care	2. core car care	3. harm horn hard
4. far fork fort	5. yarn yard jar	6. cork core corn
7. torch arch porch	8. park torch porch	9. ford fork fort
10. stare star store	11. star store stare	12. stork storm starch
13. harm horn horse	14. thorn throne tart	15. fork fifty forty

OR

Read the words that are part of each rhyme. Choose the word from the box that will finish the rhyme. Print the word on the line.

1. Oh! What a chore To go to the —.	_____ store _____	score store snore
2. The men are apt to scorch The oak tree with that —.	_____	scorch porch torch
3. We will add up the score Before we play some —.	_____	more tore sore
4. His pants were torn By the —.	_____	torch corn thorn
5. Down the street went little Cindy. Off went her hat, since it was —.	_____	witty windy whine

Read the words that are part of each sentence. Finish the sentence by writing the words from the box in the correct order on the line.

1. Tom likes to	_____ eat sweet corn _____ .	eat corn sweet
2. Sue can play	_____ .	horn well the
3. May I sit on	_____ ?	porch swing your
4. You can get horned toads at	_____ .	store pet the
5. Did Mom forbid you to play	_____ ?	shore on the

_____

_____

IR, UR, ER

The word **skirt** has the sound of **ir**. Say the name of the picture in each box. Print **ir** on the line in the box if you hear the sound of **ir**.

1. _ir_	2. _____	3. _____
4. _____	5. _____	6. _____
7. _____	8. _____	9. _____

The word **fur** has the sound of **ur**. Say the name of the picture in each box. Print **ur** on the line in the box if you hear the sound of **ur**.

1. _ur_	2. _____	3. _____
4. _____	5. _____	6. _____
7. _____	8. _____	9. _____

The word **fern** has the sound of **er**. Say the name of the picture in each box. Print **er** on the line in the box if you hear the sound of **er**.

1. _er_	2. _____	3. _____
4. _____	5. _____	6. _____
7. _____	8. _____	9. _____

IR, UR, ER

Say the name of the picture in each box. Circle its name.

1.	**2.**	**3.**
born (herd)	thirty thirsty	purse curve
barn hard	thirteen throat	nurse carve
4.	**5.**	**6.**
score shirt	fern form	zone perform
scare skirt	farm burn	zebra zipper
7.	**8.**	**9.**
for far	tar fir	spark sport
fur tar	for far	spider short
10.	**11.**	**12.**
short church	rocket racket	squint square
start chore	rocker park	squirt squirrel

Say the name of the picture in each box. Circle its name.

1.

(bird)   burn

barn   port

2.

spank   sport

spark   spur

3.

borders   rubbers

barbers   robbers

4.

peach   pork

pitcher   porch

5.

thirty   forty

thirteen   party

6.

turns   tart

turtle   startle

7.

garden   girl

garment   germ

8.

torch   pork

porch   party

9.

shark   short

sharp   shirt

10.

ladder   letter

leader   border

11.

termite   turkey

target   turnip

12.

marching   morning

murmur   mermaid

Read the words that are part of each rhyme. Choose the word from the box that will finish the rhyme. Print the word on the line.

1. See the lacy fern Beyond the next —.	turn	burn turn harm
2. They were not hurt When they fell in the —.		purse dirt stir
3. Please do not squirt Water on my —.		shirt flirt dirt
4. One of the girls Wore a wig of blond —.		curves whirls curls
5. May I pet the kitten, sir, Just to hear it —?		her blur purr

Read the words that are part of each sentence. Circle the word in the box that will finish the sentence. Print the word on the line.

1. The large ____ bird ____ was not a crow or a stork.		born (bird) bark
2. The cowboy got his hat and his ____.		spurs scars store
3. ____ and ten more make forty.		Ten Twenty Thirty
4. Try to get a ____ score on each paper.		perfect park porch
5. The ____ was sharp and the car had to go slow.		cart cork curve

Say the name of the picture in each box. Circle its name.

1. (doll) dolls	2. egg eggs	3. can cans	4. jet jets
5. bug bugs	6. rake rakes	7. bike bikes	8. tie ties
9. sled sleds	10. key keys	11. toe toes	12. seal seals

Read the words that are part of each sentence. Circle the word in the box that will finish the sentence. Print the word on the line.

1. Please lend a ___pencil___ to Jim.	(pencil) pencils
2. The card cost her ten _____ .	cent cents
3. The huge _____ was happy in its cage.	bird birds
4. Why do we have two _____ by each plate?	fork forks

Suffix: ES

If a word ends in **x**, **ss**, **sh**, **ch**, we usually add **es** to form the plural.

| boxes | glasses | dishes | benches |

Form the plural of each word in each box by printing s or es on the line.

ax	**es**	egg	_____	watch	_____	wish	_____
dress	_____	thrush	_____	window	_____	bird	_____
patch	_____	kiss	_____	doll	_____	fox	_____
bead	_____	beach	_____	six	_____	cross	_____
tax	_____	chain	_____	brush	_____	branch	_____

Fill in the blank with s or es to complete each sentence.

1. The nice man gave us two pass __**es**__ to the show.

2. The girls made three wish _____ .

3. The box was full of sock _____ .

4. The birds sat on the two perch _____ .

> If a word that ends in **y** is preceded by a consonant, we usually change the **y** to **i** and add **es** to form the plural.

Print the plural for each word on the line.

1. pony	ponies	2. lily	
3. fly		4. baby	
5. sky		6. buggy	
7. story		8. city	
9. penny		10. party	

Read the words that are part of each sentence. Finish the sentence with the plural form of the word in the box. Print the plural form on the line.

1. Please, read us some _stories_.	story
2. Some cities have big _____.	park
3. We had bowls of fresh _____ at the party.	berry
4. Misty is the mother of six _____.	puppy
5. The garden is full of daisies and _____.	lily

Suffixes: S, ES, IES

Print the plural form of each word on the line.

1. lady ___ladies___	2. truck _____
3. berry _____	4. dress _____
5. pony _____	6. puppy _____
7. jet _____	8. fox _____
9. dish _____	10. beach _____

Read the words that are part of each sentence. Finish the sentence with the plural form of the word in the box. Print the plural form on the line.

1. Five of the ___girls___ went to the game on a bus.	girl
2. The puppies ate the basket of _____.	peach
3. Kate went to pick some fresh _____.	berry
4. Bob needs two _____ for his toys.	box
5. The children had to pay to ride the _____.	pony

When a word ends in a consonant plus **y**, change the **y** to **i** before adding **es** or **ed**.

Add the suffixes es and ed to each word. Print the new words on the lines.

cry	cries	cried
fry		
spy		
dry		
try		
deny		
copy		
carry		
study		
empty		
hurry		

Suffix: ED Sounded as ED

When the suffix **ed** is added to a base word ending in **d** or **t**, the suffix is pronounced **ed**, as in **planted** and **handed**.

Circle the base of each word in the list below.

melt(ed)	trusted	roasted
sorted	loaded	darted
rested	handed	landed

Read the words that are part of each sentence. Circle the word in the box that will finish the sentence. Print the word on the line.

1. Cindy __handed__ the paper to Cora.	(handed) hunted needed
2. The dog _____ across the street.	listed sorted darted
3. The teacher _____ us to behave.	trusted rusted rested
4. We _____ the letters and packages.	roasted sorted nested
5. Ted _____ on the ice.	tested squinted landed
6. The class _____ papers on three trucks.	rusted loaded lasted
7. Everyone _____ until lunchtime.	darted seated rested
8. The ice has _____ so we cannot skate.	melted tested mended

Suffix: ED Sounded as T

When the suffix **ed** is added to a base word that does not end in **d** or **t**, the suffix is sometimes pronounced **t**, as in **jumped**.

Draw a ring around the base of each word in the list below.

(leap)ed	crossed	asked
puffed	helped	rushed
ticked	fixed	packed

Read the words that are part of each sentence. Circle the word in the box that will finish the sentence. Print the word on the line.

1. Dad **rushed** to catch the bus.	crashed (rushed) crushed
2. He _____ over the fence and ran fast.	leaped peeped heaped
3. Tommy _____ his mother for some fruit.	mixed boxed asked
4. Jane _____ a large picnic lunch.	backed packed picked
5. Who _____ the dessert for the picnic?	waxed fixed taxed
6. Dick huffed and _____ to lift the big box.	pasted gifted puffed
7. When we _____ the river, the boat leaked.	crossed pressed dressed
8. We all _____ to clean up before we left.	handed helped hinted

Suffix: ED Sounded as D

When the suffix **ed** is added to a base word that does not end in **d** or **t**, the suffix is sometimes pronounced **d**, as in **rained**.

Circle the base of each word in the list below.

(drain)ed   curled   cheered   groaned   loaned

burned   dreamed   mailed   snowed

Read the words that are part of each sentence. Circle the word in the box that will finish the sentence. Print the word on the line.

1. Tom **drained** the water from the fish tank.	peeled rained (drained)
2. Then he _____ it with fresh water.	filled filmed nailed
3. Ellen _____ after she ate the green peach.	snowed groaned sealed
4. Bert _____ until his throat was sore.	cheered chilled shelled
5. Joan _____ of winning the race.	feared moaned dreamed
6. Mom _____ the log in the fireplace.	foamed teamed burned
7. The log _____ red as it burned.	sailed turned peeped
8. Have you _____ the birthday card yet?	mailed nailed failed

Read the words that are part of each sentence. Finish the sentence by adding ing to one of the base words in the box. Print the new word on the line.

1. Are you going _fishing_ with your dad?	fish wish fuss
2. Rosa is _____ on Tim in the race.	pain gain braid
3. Why are you _____ the pail with water?	fail fall fill
4. _____ hot dogs is fun.	Rest Roast Fish
5. _____ for seashells is fun, too.	Hunt Hand Help
6. The plane is just _____ on the runway.	air sea land
7. Will you be _____ the letters today?	will mail sell
8. The class is _____ a bus to go to the zoo.	make sell rent
9. _____ with your left eye is hard to do.	Jump Work Wink
10. When it is _____ we have to play inside.	sail rain nail
11. He is _____ the toy with glue.	stand mend spend

Suffixes: Final Consonant Doubled

When a short-vowel word ends in a single consonant, we usually double the consonant before adding a suffix that begins with a vowel.

Add the suffixes _ed_ and _ing_ to each of the base words. Print the new words on the lines.

1. hug	hugged	hugging
2. nod		
3. hop		
4. rip		
5. beg		
6. trim		
7. bat		
8. hum		
9. shop		
10. pop		
11. stop		

Suffixes: ED, ING

Read the words that are part of each sentence. Finish the sentence by adding ed or ing to the word in the box. Print the new word on the line.

1. The tailor **hemmed** two dresses and one skirt.	hem
2. Kim _____ her kitten.	pat
3. Are you _____ the tail on the donkey?	pin
4. Tim _____ a tune as he rode away.	hum
5. The boy _____ his new puppy.	hug
6. One dog _____ at the leg of the horse.	nip
7. Are you _____ over that spilled milk?	sob
8. Ann is _____ on her pogo stick.	hop
9. Art is _____ some plants this morning.	pot
10. Jeff is _____ water from the leaky boat.	dip
11. Grace _____ to the little girl.	nod

Suffixes: ED and ING After Silent E

When a word ends with a silent **e**, we usually drop the **e** from the base word before adding **ed** or **ing**.

Add the suffixes ed and ing to each of the base words. Print the new words on the lines.

like	liked	liking
save		
bake		
dare		
vote		
wipe		
use		
time		
share		
hike		
rake		

Suffixes: ED and ING After Silent E

Read the words that are part of each sentence. Finish the sentence by adding _ed_ or _ing_ to the word in the box. Print the new word on the line.

1. We are ___hoping___ to have snow next week.	hope
2. Tony _____ his books on his desk.	pile
3. Oh! I think that you must be _____ .	joke
4. Why is Jim _____ at that man?	stare
5. Are you _____ some more help?	hire
6. Sue _____ to her friend from school.	wave
7. Do these girls like _____ ?	hike
8. They _____ water to the top of the hill.	pipe
9. Those men are _____ road scrapers.	use
10. Dave is _____ his game with all his pals.	share
11. He _____ the lawn in the morning.	rake

Suffixes: FUL and LESS

The letters ful and less are suffixes. Draw a line under each base word listed below. Then circle each suffix.

<u>tear</u>(ful)	hopeless	careless	painful	needful
tearless	hopeful	careful	painless	needless
fearless	helpful	thankful	harmful	restless
fearful	helpless	thankless	harmless	restful

Read each sentence. Circle the word in the box that best describes what each sentence is saying.

1. Rick did not stop before he rode his bike from the driveway into the street.	(careless) careful
2. Luke was so happy with his birthday gifts. He gave his mother a big hug.	thankless thankful
3. Mike washed the dishes and took out the trash.	helpless helpful
4. The brave lady jumped into the icy river to save the baby.	fearless fearful
5. The baby sobbed when he had to go to bed.	tearless tearful
6. It was quiet and peaceful at the lake. Dan lay on a blanket and dreamed.	restless restful
7. Kate went to see the dentist. She did not feel a thing when he pulled two of her teeth.	painless painful
8. Jane would have fixed the broken teacup, but one part was missing.	hopeless hopeful

Suffixes: NESS, LY

The letters ness and ly are suffixes. Draw a line under each base word listed below. Then circle each suffix.

dark(ness)   swiftly   bravely   neatness   softness

nearly   likeness   sadness   slowly   gladly

Read the words that are part of each sentence. Finish the sentence by adding ness or ly to the word in the box. Print the new word on the line.

1. Gert stacked the cans _neatly_ in rows.	neat
2. June played a tune _____ on the organ.	soft
3. Ted felt helpless in the _____ .	dark
4. Betty chose her teammates _____ .	wise
5. The fire truck turned the corner _____ .	quick
6. Luke _____ helped his mother sweep.	glad
7. Our teacher likes _____ at all times.	neat
8. We were _____ at camp when it rained.	near
9. His _____ showed in his face.	sad

Suffixes: ER, EST

The letters er and est are suffixes. First review the rules for adding suffixes to base words. Then add er and est to each of the following words. Print the new words on the lines.

slow	slower	slowest
near		
quick		
hot		
sad		
thin		
late		
brave		
large		
happy		
shiny		

Read the words that are part of each sentence. Finish the sentence by adding er or est to the word in the box. Print the new word on the line.

1. A jet flies _____faster_____ than the fastest bird.	fast
2. That is the _____ city near here.	big
3. My pad of paper is _____ than yours.	thick
4. Why is this lamp _____ than that one?	dim
5. Dessert will be served _____.	late
6. Here is the _____ spot on the beach.	shady
7. José has the _____ desk of all.	neat
8. This is the _____ part of the river.	wide
9. The peacock is the _____ bird of all.	pretty
10. It is _____ in summer than winter.	hot
11. Friday was the _____ day of the week.	sunny

Review of Suffixes: FUL, LESS, NESS, LY, ER, EST

Read the words that are part of each sentence. Finish the sentence by adding one of the suffixes above to the word in the box. Print the new word on the line.

1. We must be _careful_ crossing the street.	care
2. Today is _____ than yesterday.	hot
3. The deer raced _____ across the road.	swift
4. Bob is _____ than ever.	happy
5. This is the _____ egg I ever ate.	large
6. Her broken leg was _____ .	pain
7. Ann is the _____ runner on our team.	fast
8. A baby bird is little and _____ .	help
9. John won a prize for _____ .	neat
10. This is the _____ kitten of all.	pretty
11. We tried to fix it, but it was _____ .	hope

Contractions with Will

Draw a line from the two words in the first column in each box to the one word in the second column that has the same meaning. The words in the second column are called <u>contractions</u>.

1.

I will   he'll

they will   I'll

he will   they'll

2.

we will   she'll

she will   you'll

you will   we'll

Print the contraction for each pair of words on the line.

1. you will   you'll   2. we will ___

3. he will ___   4. they will ___

5. she will ___   6. I will ___

Read each sentence below. Underline the contractions. Choose the correct meaning for each contraction from the list just above. Print the meaning on the line next to the sentence.

1. <u>He'll</u> be in swimming class until six o'clock.   He will

2. If you'll go to the show, we'll go, too. ___

3. She'll stand before me, and I'll stand before you. ___

4. They'll all help with the party plans. ___

Contractions with Not

Draw a line from the two words in the first column in each box to the one word in the second column that has the same meaning.

1.		2.	
is not	didn't	are not	aren't
did not	isn't	has not	don't
have not	haven't	do not	hasn't

Print the contraction for each pair of words on the line.

1. has not	**hasn't**	2. did not	
3. is not		4. have not	
5. are not		6. do not	

Read each sentence below. Underline the contractions. Choose the correct meaning for each contraction from the list just above. Print the meaning on the line next to the sentence.

1. Tom isn't tired like the rest of us.	**is not**
2. Peggy hasn't had her skates fixed.	
3. Why don't we go there if they haven't time to come here?	
4. Jim didn't tell us that June and Bill aren't in the race.	

Contractions with Is and Are

Draw a line from the two words in the first column in each box to the one word in the second column that has the same meaning.

1.		2.	
he is	it's	we are	you're
she is	he's	you are	we're
it is	she's	they are	they're

Print the contraction for each pair of words on the line.

1. you are	_you're_	2. she is	_____
3. he is	_____	4. they are	_____
5. we are	_____	6. it is	_____

Read each sentence below. Underline the contractions. Choose the correct meaning for each contraction from the list just above. Print the meaning on the line next to the sentence.

1. Most of us think it's too cold to skate.	_it is_
2. You're the one we're trying to cheer up.	_____
3. They're the ones who made a fuss.	_____
4. He's crying, but she's not.	_____

Contractions with Am, Have, Us

Draw a line from the two words in the first column in each box to the one word in the second column that has the same meaning.

1.

I am   let's

I have   I've

let us   I'm

2.

we have   you've

you have   they've

they have   we've

Print the contraction for each pair of words on the line.

1. you have _you've_

2. they have _____

3. I have _____

4. I am _____

5. we have _____

6. let us _____

Read each sentence below. Underline the contractions. Choose the correct meaning for each contraction from the list just above. Print the meaning on the line next to the sentence.

1. You've run onto the soft cement with your bike. _you have_

2. Let's do the dishes while I'm willing to help you. _____

3. I've been more helpful than you've been. _____

4. We've been as careless as they've been. _____

Read the words that are part of each sentence. Circle the pair of words in the box that will finish the sentence. Print the contraction for those words on the line. Some sentences need two contractions.

1. _They've_ played that tune twice.	~~They have~~ (circled) They will They are
2. My wagon _____ larger than yours.	did not is not have not
3. _____ the safest way to travel.	Is not I am It is
4. _____ you in charge of the program?	Are not Did not Has not
5. _____ sing while they dance.	He will He is We are
6. This horse _____ win first prize.	have not did not he is
7. _____ the smartest girl in the class.	I will She is I have
8. _____ see if _____ stronger than I.	let us she has you are
9. _____ neatly stacked the games in a pile.	You will We have We are
10. _____ going to the picnic, so _____ see you.	I have I am I will
11. _____ playing ball.	Is not Do not She is

Vowel Digraph Sound: OO

The word zoo has one sound of the vowel digraph oo. Say the name of the picture in each box. Circle each picture with a name that has the sound of oo, as in zoo.

1.	2.	3.	4.
5.	6.	7.	8.
9.	10.	11.	12.
13.	14.	15.	16.
17.	18.	19.	20.

Say the name of the picture in each box. Circle its name.

1.	(boots) boost boat	2.	hoof root roof	3.	noon moon moan
4.	too moo zoo	5.	toad road rose	6.	fools tools tooth
7.	toes hoes hose	8.	hoop hoe hope	9.	spool soon spoon
10.	boom broom booth	11.	stoop stole stool	12.	bowl blow bows
13.	spool pole pool	14.	roast goose roost	15.	soothe tooth booth

Read the words that are part of each sentence. Circle the word in the box that will finish the sentence. Print the word on the line.

1. Sam and Rosa rode the bus to the __ZOO__ .	too moo (zoo)
2. Jack ate the most _____ at the picnic.	food fool pool
3. The rooster crows each morning in his _____ .	cool boot coop
4. Let's _____ a rocket to the moon!	loose shoot shot
5. I can't eat this food. My tooth is too _____ .	tooth booth loose
6. This is the shadiest place if you wish to be _____ .	cool coal coop
7. I had to _____ to pick up the broom.	shoot spoon stoop
8. Darkness slowly filled the tiny _____ .	broom room gloom
9. The balloon rose quickly, then landed on the _____ .	tool roof root
10. There is a _____ board in the tool room.	loot moose loose
11. He can't find his left _____ .	spool boot moon

Vowel Digraph Sound: OO

The word **book** has the other sound of the vowel digraph **oo**. Say the name of the picture in each box. Circle each picture with a name that has the sound of **oo**, as in **book**.

1.	2.	3.	4.
5.	6.	7.	8.
9.	10.	11.	12.
13.	14.	15.	16.
17.	18.	19.	20.

Say the name of the picture in each box. Circle its name.

1. foot / food / boot	2. books / boots / foot	3. roots / woods / wools
4. mood / noon / moon	5. hood / hoof / foot	6. soon / zoo / moo
7. root / cook / took	8. tooth / fools / tools	9. hook / look / book
10. footprint / footpath / football	11. look / hook / book	12. book / hook / brook
13. cooler / coops / cookies	14. woodshed / woodsman / woodpile	15. woodcutter / woodpecker / woodcraft

Read the words that are part of each sentence. Circle the word in the box that will finish the sentence. Print the word on the line.

1. **Look** at the horses run.	Book ⟨Look⟩ Hook
2. One of them has hurt its _____ .	tool boot foot
3. They are shearing _____ from the sheep.	wool cool food
4. Janet took the thick _____ to school.	took book brook
5. Who can give me a _____ haircut?	good pool food
6. Please give me a _____ for my birthday.	took book look
7. May I please have some _____ carving tools, too?	wool wood hood
8. They _____ turns swinging and riding the bike.	took look book
9. Who will put the worm on the _____ for me?	look book hook
10. Dora had a jacket with a _____ on it.	food hood hoop
11. We'll camp in the woods and _____ our meals there.	cool wool cook

Vowel Digraph Sound: EA

The word **bread** has a sound of the vowel digraph **ea**. Say the name of the picture in each box. Circle each picture with a name that has the sound of **ea**, as in **bread**.

1.	2.	3.	4.
5.	6.	7.	8.
9.	10.	11.	12.
13.	14.	15.	16.
17.	18.	19.	20.

Say the name of the picture in each box. Circle its name.

1. breath teach (teeth)	2. breath thread threat	3. seat seal neat
4. leak beak peak	5. cleanser weather sweater	6. feather father leather
7. bread read dread	8. sweat met meat	9. peach poach pitch
10. heal head deal	11. beaver beater boater	12. breathing breading breakfast
13. peaches peaceful peacock	14. why wheat what	15. deadline headstone headline

Vowel Digraph Sound: EA

Read each question. Choose the answer from the list of words. Print the answer on the line in the box.

bread	sweater	head
meadow	breath	thread
cleanser	breakfast	weather

1. What do you put on when it is cool? —— sweater

2. What is good and bad, but cannot be changed?

3. What changes to white when it is cold? Then you can see it.

4. What is attached to your body and tells you what to do?

5. What tastes good with jelly and peanut butter spread on it?

6. Which meal may have bacon, eggs, toast, juice, and milk?

7. What can you use to stitch the rip in your shirt?

8. What is big and green? Sheep like to visit it.

9. What can you use to clean the ring that you left in the bathtub?

Vowel Digraph Sounds: AU, AW

The vowel digraph <u>au</u> in <u>laundry</u> and the vowel digraph <u>aw</u> in <u>saw</u> have the same sound. Say the name of the picture in each box. Circle each picture with a name that has the sound that <u>au</u> and <u>aw</u> share.

1.	2.	3.	4.
5.	6.	7.	8.
9.	10.	11.	12.
13.	14.	15.	16.
17.	18.	19.	20.

Say the name of the picture in each box. Circle its name.

1.	(paw) / jaw / law	2.	into / ant / auto	3.	was / saw / raw
4.	ways / yawn / yarn	5.	claw / clam / draw	6.	fan / fun / fawn
7.	booster / coaster / rooster	8.	straw / draw / drag	9.	hawk / hark / hard
10.	supper / saucer / saucepan	11.	hook / cook / book	12.	chill / shell / shawl
13.	feather / leather / father	14.	aiming / ironing / awning	15.	message / passage / sausage

Read each question below. Choose the answer from the list of words.
Print the answer on the line in the box.

lawn	yawn	dawn
sawdust	auto	fawn
because	crawl	awning

1. What can you ride in?　　　　　auto

2. What is the beginning
   of each day?

3. What is made when wood is cut?

4. What do babies like to do?

5. What is green in summer, but
   has a blanket of snow in winter?

6. What animal will grow up
   to be a deer?

7. What can you say
   when asked, "Why?"

8. What do you do
   when you get sleepy?

9. What can keep the sun
   out of a room?

Review of Vowel Digraphs

Read the words that are part of each sentence. Circle the word in the box that will finish the sentence. Print the word on the line.

1. The weather is hot in _August_ .	March (August) May
2. Camping is good _____ of the weather.	between saucer because
3. Please turn off the leaky _____ .	faucet fancy furnace
4. Fido must not eat _____ meat.	saw was raw
5. Grace toasted the _____ .	lead bread tread
6. Let's _____ a good birthday gift for Ken.	shoot chose choose
7. Jane _____ a book back to the library.	book took look
8. The _____ darted into the woods.	fan fawn farm
9. The class _____ the workers make steel .	saw was sad
10. A stalled car _____ a traffic jam .	hauled paused caused
11. Tom handed his uncle the _____ .	raw law saw

Diphthong Sounds: OW, OU

The diphthong <u>ow</u> in <u>cow</u> and the diphthong <u>ou</u> in <u>snout</u> can have the same sound. Say the name of the picture in each box. Circle each picture with a name that has the sound <u>ow</u> and <u>ou</u> share.

1.	2.	3.	4.
5.	6.	7.	8.
9.	10.	11.	12.
13.	14.	15.	16. ae iou
17.	18.	19.	20.

Say the name of the picture in each box. Circle its name.

1. (cow) crow crowd	2. mouth moose mouse	3. clowns cloud couch
4. prowl plow pout	5. owe owl low	6. proud plow blouse
7. crowd clown crown	8. snout snoop scour	9. throw bowl towel
10. blouse hound house	11. scowl clown crown	12. flower flow blow
13. scour scout sprout	14. ae iou scowls towels vowels	15. flower shouter shower

Diphthong Sounds: OW, OU

Read each question. Choose the answer from the list below. Print the answer on the line in the box.

flower	flour	brown
out	owl	mouth
bounce	round	now

1. What means the same as <u>not in</u>?

   out

2. What is the color of muddy water?

3. What is the shape of the tire on a wagon?

4. What is a wise bird with big eyes?

5. What can you say when asked, "When?"

6. What can you use to make cakes, pies, and bread?

7. What does Timmy water so that it will grow?

8. What is one way that you play with a ball?

9. What part of your face do you use for eating?

Read the words that are part of each sentence. Circle the word in the box that will finish the sentence. Print the word on the line.

1. Did you throw pennies **down** the well?	brown (down) cow
2. The sound of the horn was _____ and clear.	loud shout mouth
3. The _____ lemon made his mouth pucker.	our sour scout
4. Did my dog _____ at you?	towel grow growl
5. " _____ ! That hurts," said Tommy.	Ouch Our Couch
6. Do you have a shower in your _____ ?	hose towel house
7. Mike dried himself quickly with a _____ .	vowel tower towel
8. Carol _____ pinned on the badge.	loudly proudly pretty
9. I _____ pie in my lunch box.	hound found flour
10. The crowd clapped as the _____ acted silly.	cloud clown crowd
11. Did you hear that loud _____ ?	round brown sound

Crossword Puzzle Review

Fill in the crossword puzzle. The sounds you learned in this book will help you. Look at the clues in parentheses. The first one has been done for you.

Across

1. a warning from a dog (ow diphthong)
3. worn on feet (sh digraph)
5. a bird that stays up all night (ow diphthong)
8. part of your body used to wave hello (short a)
9. worn to keep a hand warm (two-syllable word)
10. instrument played with two sticks (r blend)
11. opposite of out (short i)
12. tool to gather leaves on the ground (silent e)
14. long green food (soft c)

Down

1. opposite of stop (long o)
2. opposite of quiet (ou diphthong)
3. one of the s blends
4. used to tie things together (s blend)
6. sharp part of a rose plant (th digraph)
7. a cereal used to make cookies (long vowel compound)
10. used to hold food (sh digraph)
13. vehicle (hard c)

The diphthong <u>oy</u> in <u>boy</u> and the diphthong <u>oi</u> in <u>oil</u> have the same sound.
Say the name of the picture in each box. Circle each picture with a name
that has the sound that <u>oy</u> and <u>oi</u> share.

1.	2.	3.	4.
5.	6.	7.	8.
9.	10.	11.	12.
13.	14.	15.	16.
17.	18.	19. ae iou	20.

Say the name of the picture in each box. Circle its name.

| 1. (oil) oar | 2. out our | boy boil | 3. foil soil | pay joy | toy boy |
| 4. rains joins | coins coils | 5. tops taps | boys toys | 6. paint point | pound found |

Diphthong Sounds: OY, OI

Read each question. Choose the answer from the list below. Print the answer on the line in the box.

choice	moist	soil
Roy	point	oyster
broil	toys	poison ivy

1. What is one way to cook meat? — — — — — — broil — — — — — —

2. What do children like to play with? — — — — — — — — — — — — — — — —

3. What is the sharp end of a pin? — — — — — — — — — — — — — — — —

4. What do you call a little animal who lives under the water? — — — — — — — — — — — — — — — —

5. What is another word for dirt? — — — — — — — — — — — — — — — —

6. What is found in the woods that you must stay away from? — — — — — — — — — — — — — — — —

7. What is a boy's name? — — — — — — — — — — — — — — — —

8. You can choose this toy or that toy. What do you have? — — — — — — — — — — — — — — — —

9. How do your eyes get when you are about to cry? — — — — — — — — — — — — — — — —

Diphthong Sound: EW

The word **blew** has the sound of the diphthong **ew**. Say the name of the picture in each box. Circle each picture with a name that has the sound of **ew**.

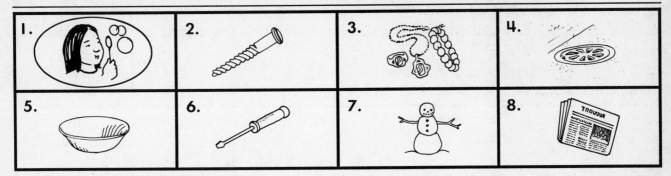

| 1. | 2. | 3. | 4. |
| 5. | 6. | 7. | 8. |

Read each question. Choose the answer from the list below. Print the answer on the line in the box.

chew   mew   stew   flew   few   news   blew

1. What must you do to your food before you swallow it?   _chew_

2. What did the wind do to the kite?

3. How did the birds travel to the south?

4. What is the sound made by a cat?

5. If you didn't have many coins, how many would you have?

6. What may be good or bad? You hear about it in many ways.

7. What can you eat?

Diphthong Sound: EW

Read the words that are part of each sentence. Circle the word in the box that will finish the sentence. Print the word on the line.

1. Jack ___grew___ tall.	blew (grew) dew
2. Who _____ this chewing gum on the floor?	screw stew threw
3. Where did you get that shiny _____ coin?	new now mew
4. The wind _____ hard, but the house didn't fall.	few blew blow
5. We joined two blocks of wood with a _____.	threw new screw
6. Tom's uncle _____ cartoons for the class.	chew grow drew
7. The _____ in the morning sun looked like jewels.	do dew few
8. Did you hear the cat _____?	pew grew mew
9. Just a _____ children can make a lot of noise.	dew few flew
10. Manny wore his _____ winter coat.	grew new drew
11. The _____ got on the ship.	chew crew brew

Diphthongs

Read the words that are part of each rhyme. Choose the word from the box that will finish the rhyme. Print the word on the line.

1. A sly old mouse Came into the _____.	house	home hound house
2. He ate some beef stew And had breadcrumbs, a _____.		new few coil
3. The cat and the boy Were busy with a _____.		toy threw towel
4. The mouse never made a sound So he was never _____.		found round frown
5. The cat felt blue, And so it cried, " _____."		few mew wow

Read the words that are part of each sentence. Finish the sentence by writing the words from the box in the correct order.

1. The bike is _____ shiny and new _____.		and new shiny
2. I will invite _____.		the all boys
3. The shop is on the main _____.		town in street
4. Juan will dress _____.		a clown like
5. Did you buy a ticket _____ ?		coins your with

Diphthongs

Read the short story. Then answer the questions at the bottom of the page.

Floyd's Birthday Surprise

On Floyd's seventh birthday he had a party. All the boys and girls from his class were invited.

Jim and Joy came first with a toy for Floyd. Soon the other boys and girls came. One gave a stuffed owl to Floyd. Another gave him a clown puppet. Joyce gave him a gift of a tame white mouse.

The boys and girls sang, "Happy Birthday." They ate huge mounds of ice cream with cake.

Soon it was time for games. The boys and girls shouted as they threw coins into a bowl and pinned the tail on the donkey. Then they went outside to play tag around the swimming pool. Around and around they went, making more and more noise as they ran.

Suddenly, the noise stopped. There wasn't a sound. Dad looked out and saw the children pointing at the water. He knew what must have happened.

Quickly, he ran outside. "We didn't plan to scare you," he said. "This seal is our surprise gift to Floyd."

All of the boys and girls shouted with glee, and when they left the party, they agreed that they had never had so much fun.

1. What stuffed animal did Floyd get for a gift?	OWl
2. What live animal did Joyce give Floyd?	
3. In one game the children used a bowl and some coins. What did they do with the coins?	
4. What stopped when the boys and girls saw the seal in the pool?	

KN

The letters kn have the sound of n. The k is silent. Say the name of the picture in each box. Circle its name.

1. (knot) knit	2. kneel knife	3. know knob
4. knew knock	5. knit knot	6. catfish knapsack

Read each question below. Choose the answer from the list of words.
Print the answer on the line in the box.

knob   knife   know   knees   knock

1. I am a rap on a door. What am I? —————— knock ————

2. I am what you turn to open most doors. ————————————

3. I mean the same as <u>to be sure of</u>. ——————————

4. I am used in the kitchen. A scout uses me in the woods. You all use me at dinner. What am I?

5. I am part of your legs. ——————————————

KN

Read the words that are part of each sentence. Write the numeral of the word in the box that will finish the sentence.

1.

Do you __3__ how to knit?

Dave cut some branches with his _____.

Martha is _____ a sweater for her sister.

How many _____ have you tied in this rope?

1. knitting
2. knots
3. know
4. knife

2.

Slowly, I saw the _____ turn.

The _____ on the door was loud and clear.

Sammy _____ down to look under his bed.

Please, get on your _____ and look for my penny.

1. knock
2. knelt
3. knob
4. knees

3.

Sue used her _____ to carve a boat out of wood.

The _____ on the dresser fell to the floor.

Jenny had _____ about the surprise for a long time.

Tom's _____ shook as he read his report to the class.

1. known
2. knees
3. knife
4. knickknacks

4.

The boxing match ended with a _____.

Pat scraped the skin off his _____.

The _____ on the door does not work.

Uncle Dan got me a _____ to use on hikes.

1. knuckles
2. knockout
3. knapsack
4. knob

The letters wr have the sound of r. The w is silent. Say the name of the picture in each box. Circle its name.

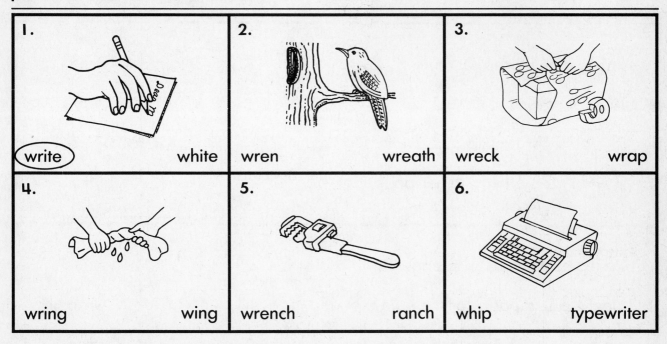

1. (write)　　white

2. wren　　wreath

3. wreck　　wrap

4. wring　　wing

5. wrench　　ranch

6. whip　　typewriter

Read each riddle below. Choose the answer from the list of words. Print the answer on the line in the box.

wren　　wrapper　　wreck　　wreath　　wrist

1. I may be made of flowers and leaves. I form a big ring. What am I?　　wreath

2. I am the paper around a candy bar. What am I?

3. I am the part of your arm next to your hand. What am I?

4. If you are a careless driver, you will soon know me. What am I?

5. I am a small bird with a twitching tail and a nice song. What am I?

WR

Read the words that are part of each sentence. Write the numeral of the word that will finish the sentence.

1.

I have a new bracelet on my __4__.

The train never had a _____.

Do you know how to _____ letters?

Elaine _____ a letter to her pal, Jeff.

1. write
2. wrote
3. wreck
4. wrist

2.

I need some red _____ paper.

Ned _____ a poem for the school paper.

He has _____ stories and books, too.

Where does the _____ have its nest?

1. written
2. wrapping
3. wren
4. wrote

3.

Don _____ a package to send to Joe.

Joan fell and broke her_____.

Bill _____ for tickets to the circus.

Please _____ the water out of the cloth.

1. wrist
2. wrapped
3. wring
4. wrote

4.

We used a _____ to fix the sink.

Aunt Flora wore a _____ of roses in her hair.

The _____ pulled the car out of the ditch.

"It is _____ to tell a lie," said Nate to Abe.

1. wrecker
2. wreath
3. wrong
4. wrench

Read the short story. Then answer the questions at the bottom of the page.

The Fun Fair

The children planned the school fun fair. Each class made a booth for playing games or for making crafts.

Merle is in the third grade. Her class made a game booth. They set up a table and covered it with a cloth. They filled a large plastic bottle with sudsy water. When people came to their booth, the children gave each person a bubble wand to dip in the bottle. The person who blew the biggest bubble was the winner of the game. The prize was a whistle.

Todd is in the fourth grade. His class had a craft booth. They set up a table and chairs. They put out paper and pans of paints. When people came to their booth, they made a print. Each person took a slice of cut up vegetable or apple. They dipped their slices into the paints and pressed them on their papers. They had to handle the slices carefully to make a clear print.

Mike's fifth-grade class made a booth for turtle races. They made a track with boards. Each little turtle had its own slot. When Mike blew a whistle the race began. The turtles began to waddle down the track. Mike had no trouble guessing which turtle would win the race.

Everyone had a good time. They all agreed to have a fun fair each year.

---

1. A prize was given for the biggest _____.

2. The prize was a _____.

3. An art print was made with a slice of cut-up vegetable or _____.

4. The race was won by the fastest _____.

Word Ending: LE

Read each question. Choose the answer from the list of words. Print the answer on the line in the box.

| bubbles | marbles | pineapple | uncle | table |
| teakettle | stable | needle | buckle | purple |

1. What has one eye but can't see? — — — **needle** — — —

2. What has four legs but no feet?

3. What can you use to play a game?

4. I'm filled with water and placed on the fire. When water bubbles, I whistle. What am I?

5. They float like feathers and are full of air. What are they?

6. What looks like a huge pine cone and is good to eat?

7. What color do red and blue make?

8. What is your father's or your mother's brother to you?

9. I am a home for horses. What is my name?

10. What holds a belt together?

Prefix: RE

The word <u>refill</u> is <u>re</u> + <u>fill</u>. **Re** is a prefix, and <u>fill</u> is the base word. A
prefix is a word part that is added to the beginning of a base word. Circle
the prefix in each word below. Underline the base word.

(re)read	remake	repaint	rewrite
respell	reprint	reseal	rewax
renew	reclaim	recount	retell
refill	repay	renumber	repack

**Read each sentence. Choose the one word from the list above that could
be used to make the sentence shorter. Print that word on the line.**

1. When I tell the story again, I will act it out.	retell
2. Take a slice of bread, but seal the wrapper again.	
3. The gas tank is empty, so we will have to fill it again.	
4. After we repaint the walls, we will wax the floors again.	
5. Write your name again until you can write it well.	
6. Ann, please read the sentence in a louder voice.	
7. The next time, we will make valentines on good paper.	
8. I counted the coins, but I will have to count them again.	

Prefix: UN

The word **unwise** is **un** + **wise**. **Un** is a prefix, and **wise** is the base word.
Circle the prefix of each word below. Underline the base word.

(un)tie	unwrap	untidy	unhappy
unlock	undress	unfair	unselfish
unpin	unload	unwilling	unsafe
unpack	unscrew	untrue	unable

Read the words that are part of each sentence. Then circle the word that will finish the sentence. Print the word on the line.

1. It is time to _____ and go to bed.	unpin unlock (undress)	undress
2. You must wait until your birthday to _____ the gifts.	unwrap unscrew unsafe	
3. Some people tell stories that are _____ .	untie untrue untidy	
4. It is _____ to play too near the river.	unable unsafe unfair	
5. Mike was _____ and gave Kim some of his lunch.	unselfish unfair unwilling	
6. Bill cannot _____ the knot in the kite string.	unpin unpack untie	
7. The workers will _____ the truck at the dock.	unlock unload unwrap	
8. Are you _____ because you lost the game?	unselfish unwilling unhappy	

The word **disagree** is **dis** + **agree**. **Dis** is a prefix, and **agree** is the base word. Circle the prefix of each word below. Underline the base word.

(dis)<u>appear</u>	displease	disorder
dislike	disappoint	disagree
dishonest	dismount	disgrace

Read the words that are part of each sentence. Then circle the word that will finish the sentence. Print the word on the line.

1. When bubbles pop, you say that they _____ .	(disappear) disturb distant	disappear
2. When you do not like a thing, you say you _____ it.	disturb dislike discuss	
3. Try to be quiet so that you will not _____ the baby.	disturb disabled disputed	
4. If our desks are not neat, we say that they are in ____ .	dismiss dispute disorder	
5. If you do something mean, it will _____ someone.	disappear disinfect displease	
6. If Bob and Joan do not agree, we say they _____ .	disagree disappear disorder	
7. At the end of your ride on a horse, you must _____ .	disloyal disagree dismount	
8. When you throw something away, you _____ it.	discuss dishonest discard	

Prefixes: RE, UN, DIS

In each sentence, one of the prefixes in the box can be added to the word following the blank space. Read the sentence. Circle the prefix that will make sense, and write it in the space.

1. Today we will ___**re**___ read the story that we read last week.	(re) / un
2. Do you _____ like playing marbles?	un / dis
3. It is _____ like Ted to tell a lie.	un / dis
4. Now, _____ write your letter on good paper.	re / un
5. Can you _____ screw this jar lid?	dis / un
6. Please _____ hook the screen door for your sister.	dis / un
7. The teacher will _____ miss the class at noon.	dis / re
8. Theresa will _____ load the camera with film.	dis / re
9. Remember to _____ pay the money that Dave loaned you.	un / re
10. It is _____ fair to expect me to do all of the cleaning.	un / re
11. Did you _____ lock the door?	un / dis

Synonyms

Draw a line joining the words in each box that have the same meaning or almost the same meaning.

1.		2.		3.	
bag	glad	quick	law	every	each
large	beg	tardy	late	scowl	gift
happy	sack	sharp	fast	present	aid
ask	big	rule	keen	help	frown

4.		5.		6.	
strike	jab	sick	creep	jump	fast
poke	damp	damage	ill	quit	fall
moist	hit	crawl	small	drop	stop
spoil	rot	little	hurt	quick	leap

7.		8.		9.	
auto	let	blend	mix	choose	say
look	dim	mow	cut	price	pick
allow	car	tidy	cent	remain	cost
faint	see	penny	neat	speak	stay

10.		11.		12.	
slip	sum	plaything	fun	blaze	trail
total	easy	sport	still	connect	flame
bashful	shy	quiet	toy	follow	far
simple	slide	middle	center	distant	join

Synonyms

Print s on the line beside each pair of words that has the same meaning.

1. quick fast ___s___	2. unhappy sad _____	3. little big _____
4. auto car _____	5. dry wet _____	6. present gift _____
7. look hide _____	8. crawl creep _____	9. plaything toy _____
10. slide slip _____	11. blend penny _____	12. near far _____
13. pick speak _____	14. sick ill _____	15. tardy late _____

Read each word. Then write another word that has the same meaning on the line.

1. large ___big___	2. tardy _____
3. quit _____	4. ill _____
5. quick _____	6. auto _____
7. tidy _____	8. choose _____
9. allow _____	10. distant _____

Draw a line joining the words in each box that have opposite meanings.

1.		2.		3.	
yes	on	good	little	near	wet
in	no	glad	short	fast	slow
off	down	big	sad	sick	far
up	out	tall	bad	dry	well

4.		5.		6.	
close	open	fair	untidy	thick	go
rise	frown	hard	weak	stay	thin
smile	fall	neat	unfair	gain	long
rich	poor	strong	soft	short	loss

7.		8.		9.	
follow	dull	true	fearless	clean	asleep
under	unequal	rip	noisy	full	dirty
equal	over	quiet	false	lucky	empty
sharp	lead	fearful	mend	awake	unlucky

10.		11.		12.	
sweet	winter	wise	take	safe	selfish
fresh	cold	bring	outside	unselfish	careful
summer	stale	inside	foolish	helpful	unsafe
hot	sour	first	last	careless	helpless

Antonyms

Print A on the line beside each pair of words with opposite meanings.

1. good bad a	2. shiny new	3. tall short
4. smile frown	5. poor rich	6. happy glad
7. fast quick	8. false true	9. clean dirty
10. fresh stale	11. take bring	12. quit stop
13. dress undress	14. large big	15. painless painful

Read each word. Then write on the line another word that has the opposite meaning.

1. yes no	2. thick
3. frown	4. poor
5. sick	6. dirty
7. good	8. sweet
9. first	10. summer

Homonyms

Draw a line in each box joining the words that sound the same.

1.			2.			3.		
sea		sow	to		bale	be		heel
so		sail	tale		two	blue		blew
mail		male	bail		meat	here		bee
sale		see	meet		tail	heal		hear

Read the words that are part of each sentence. Then circle the word in the box that will finish the sentence. Print the word on the line.

1. You can have fun playing these __two__ games.	too (two)
2. What is the best way to treat a blister on your _____ ?	heal heel
3. Shirley will study to _____ a doctor.	be bee
4. Please don't give me _____ much to eat.	so sow
5. Let's run to _____ Mom when she gets off the bus.	meat meet
6. The wind _____ Jack's kite up into a tree.	blew blue
7. May I ride my new _____ bike down the steep hill?	blew blue
8. This monkey has the longest _____ in the jungle.	tale tail

Homonyms

Draw a line in each box joining the words that sound the same.

1.		2.		3.	
too	fair	son	rode	pale	knew
weak	to	red	real	pane	knows
deer	week	road	read	new	pail
fare	dear	reel	sun	nose	pain

Read the words that are part of each sentence. Then circle the word in the box that will finish the sentence. Print the word on the line.

1. Helen took her ___son___ on a camping trip.	(son) / sun
2. They followed a twisting _____ over the hill.	rode / road
3. Ken turned _____ when he saw the deadly snake.	pail / pale
4. Please _____ this letter at the post office.	mail / male
5. Mary is the only one who _____ my secret.	knows / nose
6. The _____ was filled to the top with sand.	pale / pail
7. Duke used his paw to brush a bee off his _____.	nose / knows
8. José rode Topper in the horse show at the _____.	fare / fair

Homonyms

Read the words that are part of each sentence. Then circle the word in the box that will finish the sentence. Print the word on the line.

1. We may see a **deer** while we are camping.	(deer) dear
2. Do you think that we will _____ a fox, too?	sea see
3. June can catch fish in this brook with her rod and _____.	real reel
4. May we eat our meals _____ under this tree?	hear here
5. Kim _____ some people talking in the next room.	heard herd
6. Ted _____ how to swim when he was three.	knew new
7. The cave seems dark after being in the _____.	son sun
8. "Let's wait until next _____ to explore it," said Dad.	week weak
9. Linda knows how to swim and dive well, _____.	too to
10. How much is the bus _____ to town?	fair fare
11. We enjoyed telling tall _____ about the old West.	tails tales

Crossword Puzzle Review

Fill in the crossword puzzle. The sounds you learned in this book will help you. Look at the clues in parentheses. The first one has been done for you.

Across

1. hangs on a branch (ea spells long e)
3. has the same meaning as penny (soft sound of c)
5. large bird (s blend)
7. touch gently (short a)
8. has the same meaning as eat (long i)
9. dogs and cats (short e)
11. places to sleep (short e)
13. what we hear with
14. helps get things clean (long o)
15. home of birds (s blend on the end)

Down

2. the suffix used to form the plural of dish
3. a kind of heavy string (hard c)
4. something in the woods (long e)
5. a synonym for stain
6. it flies in the wind (long i)
9. things used to write and draw (short e)
10. take one giant _____ (s blend)
11. your birthday celebrates the day you were _____
12. opposite of hard